900937

How old is old
enough?

# HOW OLD IS OLD ENOUGH?
## The Ages of Rights and Responsibilities

Report No. 126

# HOW OLD IS OLD ENOUGH?
## The Ages of Rights and Responsibilities

*Formulated by the*
*Committee on Child Psychiatry*

Group for the Advancement of Psychiatry

BRUNNER/MAZEL *Publishers* • New York

**Library of Congress Cataloging-in-Publication Data**

How old is old enough? : the ages of rights and responsibilities /
    formulated by the Committee on Child Psychiatry,
    Group for the Advancement of Psychiatry.
        p.    cm. — (Report ; no. 126)
    Includes bibliographies.
    ISBN 0-87630-520-6
    1. Children's rights—United States.    2. Age (Psychology)
3. Children—Legal status, laws, etc.    4. Liability (Law)—United
States.    I. Group for the Advancement of Psychiatry.
Committee on Child Psychiatry.    II. Series: Report (Group
for the Advancement of Psychiatry : 1984) ; no. 126.
    [DNLM: 1. Age Factors.    2. Child Advocacy.    3. Social
Responsibility.    W1 RE209BR no. 126 / WA 320 H847]
RC321.G7 no. 126
[HQ789]
616.89 s—dc19
[305.2′3]
DNLM/DLC
for Library of Congress                                        88-38962
                                                                    CIP

*Published by*
BRUNNER/MAZEL, INC.
19 Union Square West
New York, New York 10003

MANUFACTURED IN THE UNITED STATES OF AMERICA

10   9   8   7   6   5   4   3   2   1

# CONTENTS

# HOW OLD IS OLD ENOUGH?
## The Ages of Rights and Responsibilities

# PROLOGUE

As you walk up to the door of the Balboa Cafe, some say the best hamburger place in all of San Francisco, you read "No One Under the Age of 21 Allowed." There is a big hard liquor bar at the Balboa, and no child, not even one who lives exclusively on hamburgers and is a leading hamburger critic of the Bay Area, can legally eat in this kind of place in the State of California until a young adult. Eighteen-year-olds can get into similar establishments in Hawaii, and for several years they could get into them in New Haven, at least until 1985 when the Connecticut legislature moved the legal age of drinking to 21.

Legal doctrine is often determined by social custom. It says that in one state at one time in history the drinking age is 18 or 21, and that's it, at least until the law decides otherwise. (Currently, for instance, the federal government is giving less highway money to any state that does not use age 21 as the legal drinking minimum.) Legal doctrine regarding age may change quite abruptly with the times, lurching forward with the passage of new statutes or reversing direction entirely when a new Supreme Court decision is handed down.

Developmental child psychiatry, on the other hand, is a field where knowledge grows more slowly, and which less frequently takes off on an entirely new track. Anna Freud, Piaget, Spitz, Erikson, Chess, Thomas, Kagan, and their many colleagues have given us insights which incrementally add to our knowledge, slowly adjusting our beliefs about development, but seldom radically upsetting our views.

1

Our expanding body of knowledge about child development often directly bears upon legal decisions in the area of children's rights, yet, more often than not, it is ignored. Perhaps our legislators and judges who handle children's rights issues do not know where and how to look up the relevant materials about psychological maturation. Perhaps decision-makers think that they intuitively know what to do—after all, they have "children of their own." Perhaps the medical libraries and the psychology stacks are too inconvenient. Perhaps, too, medical and psychological expert witnesses themselves do not have ready access to the pertinent child development data that they will need before they testify. And perhaps people simply have not thought about the psychological and developmental sides of children's rights. Certainly very little on the subject has been put to paper.

The Child Psychiatry Committee of the Group for the Advancement of Psychiatry wishes to remedy this lack of concern for child development by those who make and implement the laws. It is the hope of the committee to represent as broad an array of perspectives as possible: historical, psychoanalytic, Piagetian, phenomenologic, and biological. In this GAP report, the Committee on Child Psychiatry reviews past and current ideas, beliefs, and scientific data regarding children's developmental capacities. We also address the question of how children can be helped to achieve a mature capacity in regard to their responsibilities and accountabilities. The tasks we have set for ourselves are not easy. Some might say that in attempting to juxtapose an intricate developmental framework upon an even more tricky set of social and legal issues (each one of which has its own historical, social, cultural and political context) we are being intellectually immodest, insolent, or scornful of the complexity of the subject. In our discussions, the committee has been ever mindful of this danger; yet, it is our belief that extreme caution in this matter would have led to our saying nothing. What we have elected to do, to the best of our ability, is to present what is known or what is done in various disciplines about child rights and child accountability, discussing this in the light of what we know about development. At the end of each discussion we will summarize what appear to us to be the best conclusions that follow from what is known about the issue.

Child psychiatrists, we believe, must concern themselves with children's rights. Child psychiatrists will be called upon to participate in the process of social decision-making as specialized "interpreters" of the child. An understanding of children's behavioral motivation, shifting mental states, and developing emotional and cognitive capacities is essential to the process of reaching rational and humane decisions in the courts and by governmental bodies. What may be appropriate for a 2-year-old is not at all acceptable for a 7-year-old and even less so for a teenager. Information is now available on how children think and act at various stages of their youth, but those who make crucial decisions for youngsters often proceed without heeding any of this. Child psychiatrists are trained in developmental principles; they know how to elicit information about the inner life and feelings of children. If, in pertinent instances, they contribute such data to families, courts, and legislators, child psychiatry may help to bring about reasonable decisions regarding children. The rights, responsibilities, and welfare of children are multidisciplinary concerns. As youngsters grow, their relevant environment expands and their intrapsychic life becomes increasingly rich. Psychiatric interpretation of these complex intrapsychic states to the child, to the parents, and to legal advocates may be crucial in helping to resolve conflicts that impinge on the youngster's future. In addition, decisions made at one time in a child's life may often need to be reconsidered at a later stage. Good intentions on the part of legislators, social welfare workers, judges, and health authorities are simply not enough. Each time the issue is raised, the rights of children must be considered within a psychological-developmental framework.

If you are called upon to testify in court, we invite you to read this monograph. If you consult to a school, a lawmaking body, a court, or directly to families, we ask you to read on. If you are interested in new developments at the interface of some very active disciplines, then you should find this monograph of considerable interest.

# 1

## A HISTORICAL PERSPECTIVE ON AGE AS A MARKER

By the law as it now stands, and has stood at least since the time of Edward the Third, the capacity of doing ill, or contracting guilt, is not so much measured by years and days, as by the strength of the delinquent's understanding and judgment. For one lad of eleven years may have as much cunning as another of fourteen. Under seven years of age an infant cannot be guilty of a felony, for then a felonious discretion is almost an impossibility in nature: but at eight years old he may be guilty of felony. Also, under fourteen, though an infant shall be prima facie adjudged to be doli capax, yet if it appears to the court that he was doli capax, and could distinguish between good and evil, he may be convicted and suffer death. Thus a girl of thirteen has been burnt for killing her mistress; and one boy of ten, and another of nine years old, who had killed their companions, had been sentenced to death, and he of ten years actually hanged. And there was an instance in the last century, when a boy of eight years old was tried at Abbington for firing two barns; and it appeared that he had malice, revenge, and cunning; he was found guilty, condemned and hanged accordingly.
> —Blackstone's Commentaries (as quoted in Platt & Diamond, 1966)

The above statement, written by a preeminent eighteenth century jurist, is barbaric indeed; yet it raises questions that remain with us today. At what age can a child be judged responsible for murder? For assault? For slander? When can a child be said to have acted with malice aforethought, to have had a "positive desire" to injure another? When should a child be judged able to understand a contract? To testify in court? To refuse medical treatment? To refuse to participate in research? At what age do various rights and responsibilities begin?

In this first chapter, we begin with an historical overview of children's rights and responsibilities, identifying fundamental beliefs which have been held for centuries in an unconscious treasury of practical knowledge. At its conclusion, we will comment in a general way upon the historical trends noted.

## A HISTORY OF CHOSEN AGES

Age is a very convenient measure of maturity. All societies segment the life cycle in some way, if only to ensure that citizens "act their age." Society has never been at a loss for setting times at which children are expected to participate, or not to participate, in various activities, rituals, or ceremonies. In this chapter, we largely restrict ourselves to the United States and Western Europe. The historical sources chronicled here read primarily as a tale of the middle and upper classes.

Although age is now the most commonly used measure of children's legal capacities, in an earlier preindustrial society people often did not know how old they were. Physical capability was more the ruling factor than was time already spent on earth. During medieval times, children's ages were considered less important than were their month, day, and hour of birth, since it was believed that astrological orbit, rather than development, accounted for a child's behaviors (Keniston, 1973). In the "olden days," the stages of life were defined in far broader terms than they are now. First century Roman law noted three stages for childhood: *infanta* (birth to 6 years), *pueritia* (7 to 13 years), and *pubertas* (14 to 20 years). In 16th and 17th century England, the word "baby" could refer to a schoolboy, and someone termed a "child" might be as old as 24 years. Even in the early 18th century, Cotton Mather distinguished only three age groups (and, at that, just for males): children, young men, and old men (Kett, 1978).

## THE NODAL AGES: 7, 14, 21

Certain childhood ages have, over the centuries, taken on special significance as landmarks of achievement. These times in a child's life hold powerful meanings for their believers, and interestingly enough, these ages are the multiples of 7: 7 years, 14 years, and 21 years.

Shapiro and Perry (1976) have noted how commonly the age of 7 plus or minus 1 has been used in various developmental and societal timetables. A scattering of other "magical" ages ($\pm$ 1 year) can also be identified in the records of the past.

Age 7 is the first of these milestones, and we will document many special functions it has taken on, in addition to serving as the dividing point for Roman childhood. Beyond age 7, its multiples—14 and 21—have also long served as historical landmarks of childhood. At the time of the Roman Empire, a boy was presumed to be able to understand the law at age 14. Between the 9th and 11th centuries, 15 was the age of majority in all of northern Europe (James, 1960; Keniston, 1973). Then at some time between the start of the 11th century and the signing of the Magna Carta in 1215, the English age of majority was moved from 15 to 21 years. For the next few hundred years, British Common Law assumed that a person was an infant until age 21, with the exception of the King of England, who attained his majority at age 18 and was never considered a minor for legislative purposes. Although motivations are often lost to the historians, and no one seems to know exactly why the age of majority rose so swiftly from 15 to 21, one suggestion has been preferred: that this swift upward move came about because 12th century knights required far greater strength and skill to manage their increasingly heavier arms and armor on horseback than did the 11th century warriors who fought on foot. Because of this change in styles of warfare, a man could no longer be a man until he reached the age of 21.

Although we often think of the demands of today's technological society as lengthening the span of childhood, there is an opposite viewpoint: that the tendency toward homogenization of different ethnic groups, rural/urban groups, and the educated/not-so-educated groups though the years has actually shortened the transit time from youth to adulthood (Keniston, 1973; Modell, Furstenberg & Hershberg, 1978). It appears that the timing of massive transitions in society's thinking about ages and rights has less to do with real chronological ages than it does with the needs of society and the skills, maturation, and volition the society perceives in and expects of its individual children and adolescents.

Because child development is not a uniform process, societies probably take modal characteristics into account rather than the entire range of behaviors associated with particular ages. Some human characteristics and skills mature at faster rates than do others. In every large group, certain persons may never attain particular abilities. These exceptions, however, do not determine the general trends.

## SEX, RELIGION, SCHOOL AND WORK

Although the public today speaks of landmark ages in terms of beginning school, starting to drive, becoming sexually active, buying liquor, joining the army, or voting, the focus of social custom was quite different in ages past. For instance, between the 15th and 17th centuries, the age at which certain articles of clothing were first worn was particularly emphasized. Boys were not switched from dresses to breeches until they reached that magic age of 7 (Schorsch, 1979).

The legal coupling of the sexes has often been linked to proper ages. In the middle ages, Canon Law decreed that a valid marriage could not take place before the age of 7, although in rich and powerful families this lower age limit could be overlooked. The keynote age of 7 also marked the point in life in 18th century colonial Massachusetts for boys to be prohibited from sleeping any longer with their sisters or with the female servants (Kett, 1978). While many persons in 16th, 17th, and 18th century England actually married in their late twenties, an English boy could legally contract for marriage at age 14, and a girl could do the same at age 12 (Pinchbeck & Hewitt, 1969). And, while we may think of younger and more venturesome sexual activity as a phenomenon of the mid 1960s and 1970s, personal testimonies and historical anecdotes from other centuries challenge that notion. Worry and concern about adolescent sexuality is not a recent phenomenon. In the 17th century, for instance, Louis XIII of France was expected to be sexually active by the age of 14 (Aries, 1962). After an evening of ribald stories with the young lords, Louis' friends, the adolescent Louis, and his new young wife were personally put to bed by his mother, the Queen. Two hours later, Louis returned to the party, refreshed after an hour of sleep and "having performed twice." The marriages of 13- and 14-year-olds were quite common in the early 17th century, though most remained unchronicled—at least not in the fashion of the record-keepers hired by Louis XIII.

Religious leaders and philosophers have had much to say over the centuries as to what ages children and youth should gain their privileges and take up their responsibilities. The great Protestant reformers, John Calvin and Charles Wesley, believed that children were naturally evil and must be dealt with harshly no matter what age they might be. The Roman Catholic Church, on the other hand, has traditionally considered the age when first communion can be received, the age of 7, to be the age of reason. Here again we see that age 7 holds special meaning in history and religion. But we can also see that the Catholic and Protestant views on children were, and perhaps still are, quite different.

Full spiritual maturity is considered by both the Jewish and Christian faiths to arrive at 13 or 14 years of age. Certain cognitive capacities do not reach maturity until this time in life (see Chapter 2) and puberty also is begun by this time. Thus, the age of $14 \pm 1$ has been set as a landmark on much more than its simple numerical value. The Torah gives the specific age of 13 for a boy's Bar Mitzvah, but interestingly, Jewish law suggests physical development (the appearance of pubic hair) as the criterion for when a young female must be separated at the synagogue from the males (*Encyclopaedia Judaica Jerusalem,* 1972). Bar Mitzvah includes a communal recognition of social maturity and an acceptance into the adult congregation at a certain age. But the custom of separation for girls is entirely dependent on maturation, not age.

Over the centuries, the age of 14 has been popular for religious conversions. Changing religions can be an expression of breaking away from one's parents or of rebelling at their religious teachings, substituting the beliefs of a chosen parent surrogate or peer. The New Testament tells us that Jesus left his own parents at the age of 12 in order to join the learned men in the Temple.

Legislators, juries, and judges have always favored specific designated ages, rather than stages of maturation or development, for establishing children's rights and responsibilities. The age of 7 is important in the history of lawmaking and adjudication. Until 1780, in England, a child above the age of 7 was considered to be an adult in matters of criminal responsibility. Also in England, the Infants Custody Act of 1839 used the age of 7 to determine when a certain parent should gain custody. Prior to the Act, all children went automatically to their fathers. The Act gave the courts permission to consider awarding children under the age of 7 to their mothers (Pinchbeck & Hewitt, 1973).

The second landmark age, of 14, also appeared commonly in custody law. In recent history, this is approximately the age at which a child's own wishes are given weight in custody determinations (Mnookin, 1978). Many states use 16 years, and some 14, as the age at which a person can, under certain circumstances, be criminally tried as an adult. A most extreme American example of this was a 1646 Massachusetts law which stated, "If any child above 16 years old and of sufficient understanding shall curse or smite their natural father or mother, they shall be put to death" (*Massachusetts Records,* 1854). Although the law appears to have told an alarming cautionary tale to colonial adolescents, there is no evidence that it was ever put to use.

The sex of a child may also determine his or her accountability before the law. For certain kinds of malfeasance, males are considered to reach adulthood before females, while in other activities (such as marriage) the opposite is true. Hofmann and Pilpel (1973) have pointed out that in New York State in 1973, while a girl was banned until age 18 from marrying without parental consent, she could legally consent to sexual intercourse at age 17, could buy contraceptives at age 16, and could obtain treatment on her own for venereal disease at any age at all. Such is the skewed effect when the law arbitrarily sets it rights and privileges by age, not by the developmental task in question.

Readiness for school has been another item defined in terms of age by the law. Aries (1962) points out that in France prior to the mid 17th century, a 7-year-old boy could begin college. Later, the lower age for college matriculation was moved to 10. Why? Some of these chronologies defy motivational analysis.

In 18th century America, universities took in students at a wide range of ages. Contrary to what one might have imagined, the children of wealthy and industrial parents began and ended their school careers at younger ages than did the children of farmers or of the less affluent (Kett, 1978). The boy destined for mercantilism needed to learn his basics quickly so that he could be apprenticed out or sent to sea.

In America, by 1890, most states required the compulsory education of children, but these laws were rarely enforced. In 1920, most states required schooling between the ages of 7 and 14 years, and by the mid-1930s, students were told to go to school until the age of 16. As truancy laws were gradually enforced, children who left school became known as "dropouts" (Tyack, 1976). Between 1880 and 1970, the median age in the United States for dropping out of school rose from 14.4 to 19.1 years (Modell et al., 1978).

Like school law, child labor law directly reflects changing social modes, financial conditions, and industrial practices. Here, chronological age is probably less crucial a factor in setting standards than physical fitness and adeptness for work, but because age is so easy to measure, it has become a provision in all legislation related to child labor (Mangold, 1924).

In England, the Factory Act of 1819 decreed that prior to 9 years of age children could not work in the mills or factories (Pinchbeck & Hewitt, 1973). Similarly, the American Child Labor Law of 1833 prohibited factory work by children younger than 9 years old. Children aged 9 to 13 years were not to work more than 48 hours per week, and those age 13 to 18 were not to work more than 68 hours per week (Kessen, 1965).

A British act of 1536 authorized every parish to redirect healthy begging children between the ages of 5 and 14 into apprenticeships with masters of various crafts (Pinchbeck & Hewitt, 1969). Here again, age 14 ± 1 seems to be a magic set-point in the choice of significant ages. In 18th century Georgia, persons from the age of 12 upwards were considered adult insofar as they could be considered eligible for "new settlers" allowance (Moore, 1840). In 18th century Massachusetts, children were expected to perform serious summer employment beginning between ages 6 and 12. The usual age for apprenticeship at that time was 14 years.

## AGE AND SUICIDE

Age has also been used as a measure in the definition of childhood psychopathology. Many beliefs about age have been perpetuated, for example, about childhood suicidal behavior. For a long time these beliefs had a great impact on the classification and clinical management of this symptom. Currently, suicide is not classified by the US Bureau of Vital Statistics as a cause of death in children who are less than 10 years old. This is based on the belief that preadolescents are not cognitively able to understand the finality of death (Frederick, 1978). In fact, many clinicians question whether suicide occurs as a childhood condition. These doubts stem from observation of the developmental immaturities in cognition and emotional expression of children and from the belief that only as children get older will they be able to carry out a plan of self-destructiveness, comprehend the meaning and consequences of the act, and experience such emotions as depression and hopelessness. Clinical care can be significantly affected by the influence of these beliefs, especially if clinicians minimize the seriousness of children's statements about wanting to die or to kill themselves.

Suicidal behavior is an example of a childhood symptom for which new concepts are evolving. The implications of recent empirical research are that many beliefs are invalid and that their practical applications ought to be reassessed. Rather than considering age or developmental level as a primary factor, research data support the concept that suicidal behavior is a very complex symptom involving the interaction of developmental, intrapsychic, and experiential factors (Pfeffer, 1986). In fact, suicidal behavior occurs in youngsters of all ages and developmental levels; it has been observed among preschool children (Rosenthal & Rosenthal, 1984), preadolescents (Ackerly, 1967; Carlson & Cantwell, 1982; Pfeffer, 1986), and adolescents (Garfinkel, Froese & Hood, 1982; Robbins & Alessi, 1985).

Clinical observation and recent research indicate that children and adolescents not only have definite concepts of death but also can express suicidal ideas clearly. Rosenthal and Rosenthal (1984) describe a 2½-year-old girl's concerns about death: The child had overdosed by taking a bottle of aspirin the morning that her chronically depressed and hypochondriacal mother had returned home from a stay in the hospital. Later, in play therapy, she reenacted the event, using a doll who found pills "in the closet" and ingested them. "What will happen to the baby now?" asked the therapist. "Baby is going to die," the child replied. She continued, "Ambulance is going to come and take baby to the hospital and then the doctor will fix her and she will be all right." Pfeffer (1986) provides many examples of preadolescents' explicit statements about death and suicide. One 7-year-old girl stated, "Sometimes I want to kill myself. When my stomach hurts I say, God, I will kill myself because I feel so bad. This year I thought of it" (p. 179).

The association between development, death concepts, and suicidal behavior has been more clearly elucidated recently. It has been known that children and adolescents have definite concepts of death, but their concepts may not include an appreciation of the processes of death or its finality. Many adolescents, in fact, may not conceptualize death as a final state (McIntire, Angle & Struppler, 1972). Studies have demonstrated that children and adolescents exhibit self-destructive behavior in conjunction with an explicit intent to die. Thus, it is now possible to formulate a definition of suicidal behavior for children and adolescents that is similar to that for adults (Pfeffer, 1986). Even if a child or adolescent does not consider death to be final, a self-destructive act can be defined as suicidal if the youngster had an intention to die, that is, if the youngster had a goal to achieve a state of death, regardless of how death is conceptualized.

The issues relevant to this discussion of suicidal behavior have wider implications, especially because they can be applied to other psychiatric symptoms such as assaultiveness, running away, and substance abuse. The manifestation of these symptoms, in a manner similar to suicidal behavior, is determined by many factors: early development experiences, intrapsychic functioning, and interpersonal relations. Thus, age and developmental level of a youngster are not the only factors that determine the way classification, characterization, and management of psychiatric symptoms in children and adolescents ought to be conceptualized.

## ANALYSIS OF THE HISTORIC AGE POTPOURRI

Throughout history, chronological age has been chosen as the convenient way to calibrate development. Three ages invariably appear as the nodal points: $7 \pm 1$ years, 12 to 14 years, and 18 to 21 years. Why? These ages, because they are used so often, must tell us something real about child development and about a child's capacity to act. How does the child psychiatrist interpret these special age landmarks?

Psychological explanations for the significance of 7 and 14 and 21 will appear in Chapter 2. Other possible explanations, such as the establishment of puberty in most children by 14, are entirely self-evident. But other factors yet, such as superstition and magic, may also have influenced the historical choices of 7, 14, and 21.

## DISCUSSION

Many of the historical anecdotes we have included in this chapter sound ridiculous to 20th century ears. Moving up the age of majority to age 21 because an 18-year-old would have a tough time boosting his armor onto the horse holds little meaning to a computer-poking, telephone-wielding, rocketry-knowledgeable populace. Yet many age-determined customs prevail today with about as little thought behind them as did King Louis XIII's special party night at the French Court.

Why, for instance, should a contemporary 14-year-old have much say in her own custody determination? "Magic" as the age may be in the 7-14-21 scheme of things, 14 is also characterized—in the 20th century at least—as an angry age, a period of rebellion. What could be more self-defeating in the long run for the average 14-year-old than to "choose" to be moved to the parent who promises less discipline, less supervision, and less talk? Yet this is the very parent whom the rebellious adolescent might choose, given a magically or historically determined voice in her own custody. At present, the 14-year-old does have that right.

What, for instance, makes a 16-year-old fully criminally responsible for his actions, as he is in many states in 20th century America? Perhaps he knows, for instance, that killing is wrong, but does he yet appreciate how strong he is? (He may or may not yet be fully physically mature.) Does he know what death is? Has he experienced tragedy, read about tragedy, felt tragedy? Has his sense of ethics, altruism, and values reached full maturity? At the very least, the ages 16 to 17 in a young offender should lead to some very serious judicial questions and considerations for the individual child, rather than to the more common quick and arbitrary remands from the juvenile system to the criminal courts. When individual cases come before the courts, they should be looked at specifically, rather than being held up to the light of a general, arbitrary age expectation.

Choosing the ages 7, 14 and 21 makes some general developmental sense, as we shall see in Chapter 2, when we consider cognitive and emotional development. But the most sensible court decisions would come from individual, case-by-case consideration. What a certain child can do now and what he or she is ready to do next should direct our decisions, not some ancient age measure. Children's cognitive, emotional, spiritual, and physical maturities do not necessarily keep pace, one with the other. Thus, an 11-year-old may be quite capable of matriculating in physics at the University of Chicago or at Yale University, yet entirely incapable of rational decisions as to custody or of "malice aforethought" when it comes to an attack upon another. An 11-year-old may still be physically incapable of ejaculations, yet highly knowledgeable about and even preoccupied with sex. This same 11-year-old may not yet be able to reach the gas pedal of an automobile and even too short to be allowed on the roller coaster.

Society requires that children be fitted into slots. General policies must be set. So it is these slots that will concern us most. We will examine and critique several of them in the course of this report. But suffice it to say, at this point, that the very specific and individual spotlight, which we believe our civil and criminal judges must put to each and every child who comes before them, cannot be applied to the mass of children to whom we direct our social policies and our laws. Instead, some cognitive and emotional framework must stand at the base of these policies so that, rather than relying on magic and the unknown, our rules will reflect what is scientific and known about children.

## REFERENCES

Ackerly, W.C. (1967). Latency-age children who threaten or attempt to kill themselves. *Journal of the American Academy of Child Psychiatry, 6,* 242–261.

Aries, P. (1962). *Centuries of childhood: A social history of family life.* New York: Knopf.

Carlson, G.A., & Cantwell, D.P. (1982) Suicidal behavior and depression in children and adolescents. *Journal of the American Academy of Child Psychiatry, 21,* 361–368.

*Encyclopaedia Judaica Jerusalem* (Vol. 4). (1972). Jerusalem: Keter.

Frederick, C.J. (1978). Current trends in suicidal behavior in the United States. *American Journal of Psychotherapy, 32,* 172–200.

Garfinkel, B.D., Froese, A., & Hood, J. (1982). Suicide attempts in children and adolescents. *American Journal of Psychiatry, 139,* 1257–1261.

Hofmann, A.D., & Pilpel, H.F. (1973). The legal rights of minors. *Pediatric Clinics of North America, 20*(4), 989–1004.

James, T.E. (1960). The age of majority. *American Journal of Legal History, 4,* 22–33.

Keniston, K. (1973). Psychological development and historical change. In T.K. Rabb & R.I. Rotberg (Eds.), *The family in history* (pp. 143–157). Cambridge, MA: Massachusetts Institute of Technology.

Kessen, W. (1965). *The child.* New York: John Wiley & Sons.

Kett, J.F. (1978). The stages of life. In M. Gordon (Ed.), *The American family in social-historical perspective* (pp. 166–191). New York: St. Martins Press.

Mangold, G.B. (1924). *Problems of child welfare.* New York: Macmillan.

*Massachusetts Records,* III. (1854). p. 101.

McIntire, A., Angle, C., & Struppler, L. (1972). The concept. *Journal of Disorders of Children, 123,* 527–532.

Mnookin, R.M. (1978). *Child, family and state: Problems and materials on children and the law.* Boston: Little, Brown.

Modell, J., Furstenberg, Jr., F.F., & Hershberg, T. (1978). Social change and transitions to adulthood in historical perspective. In M. Gordon (Ed.), *The American Family in Social-Historical Perspective* (pp. 192–219). New York: St. Martins Press.

Moore, F. (1840). A voyage to Georgia begun in the year 1735. In *Collections of the Georgia Historical Society,* (Vol. I, pp. 80–81).

Pfeffer, C.R. (1986). *The suicidal child.* New York: Guilford Press.

Pinchbeck, I., & Hewitt, M. (1969). *Children in English society,* Toronto: University of Toronto Press.

Pinchbeck, I., & Hewitt, M. (1973). *Children in English society* (Vol. 2). London: Routledge & Kegan Paul.

Platt, A., & Diamond, B.L. (1966). The origins of the "right and wrong" test of criminal responsibility and the subsequent development in the United States, A historical survey, Section IV: Criminal responsibility of children. *California Law Review, 54,* 1227–1260.

Robbins, D.R., & Alessi, N.E. (1985). Depressive symptoms and suicidal behavior in adolescents. *American Journal of Psychiatry, 142,* 588–592.

Rosenthal, P.A., & Rosenthal, S. (1984). Suicidal behavior by preschool children. *American Journal of Psychiatry, 141,* 520–525.

Schorsch, A. (1979). *Images of childhood: An illustrated social history.* New York: Mayflower.

Shapiro, T., & Perry, R. (1976). Latency revisited: The age 7 plus or minus 1. *Psychoanalytic Studies of the Child, 31,* 79–105.

Tyack, D.B. (1976). Ways of seeing: An essay on the history of compulsory schooling. *Harvard Educational Review, 46,* 355–389.

# 2

## THE AGES OF REASON AND ACCOUNTABILITY

As was noted in Chapter 1, the ages of 7, 14, and 21 appear again and again, at least in Western societies, as important transition periods in development. There are many reasons why society might choose these three ages as important defining levels of legal maturity: an instinctive belief in the magical 7s, common sense about children, legal expediency, tradition, observation of the onset of puberty, observation of the age at which full size is achieved, and perhaps even some recognition of the stages of thinking capacity in the child. This chapter will focus on this last factor, cognitive development, and on another factor, emotional development, which very seldom find their way into legal or societal expectations of youth. The ages that will be identified as important transition points in thinking styles correspond strikingly to the ages that have been identified as important from a legal and social viewpoint. This coincidence between oral tradition, legal history, psychological shift in cognitive style, and relative emotional maturity testifies to the general wisdom of the collective "common sense." On the other hand, there are serious discrepancies between the cool logic available to the 14-year-old and the emotional storms that characterize this same age. These discrepancies must be kept in mind as one reads on.

## STAGES IN COGNITIVE AND EMOTIONAL DEVELOPMENT

Within the past several decades, cognitive psychologists have actively observed the process of how children perceive and reason. While there has been an outpouring since the 1960s of new material on the subject of infantile and childhood perception, language, and symbolic thought (for reviews see Appleton et al 1975; Haith & Campos, 1977; Niemark, 1975), the model of cognitive development proposed by Jean Piaget (see Flavel, 1973; Gruber & Voneche, 1977, for overviews of Piaget's work) remains a particularly important theoretical guide to a child's thinking processes, and, when modified using the ideas of more recent cognitive theorists and researchers, provides a framework to better understand how children think. This model, because of its historical significance and because it has served as a foundation for much of the recent work in the field, will be presented in some detail in this report. We will also attend to complementary data derived from psychodynamic formulations to account for parallel factors of emotional development that color cognitive performance. Where appropriate we will comment on recent findings which modify Piaget's original concepts (see Flavell, 1985; Gardner, 1986) or which add to our understanding of cognitive development (see Case, 1985; Fischer, 1980; Siegler 1986; Sternberg, 1984).

For the most part, Piaget did not develop his model using the research designs and statistical methods of the mid-twentieth century. Rather he watched, interviewed, and questioned children, inviting them to solve various tasks, and asking them why they did such-and-such (all the while attempting to understand what mental processes were at work). Piaget came to an integrated scheme of developmental tasks and landmark ages at which youngsters could perform these operations. His research method holds much in common with the flexible open-ended techniques used today by child psychiatrists in evaluating and treating patients. Studies that followed after Piaget, including cross-cultural investigations (see Glick, 1975, for a review), have confirmed that the Piagetian model is still sound. While the ages at which children can understand and "solve" various tasks can be shown to vary depending on the manner in which the task in question is presented by the experimenter, the universal conclusion Piaget reached was that there are cognitive capacities which are extremely rare before certain ages, and other capacities which become available to children only at later stages of development. Six-month-old babies, for example, do not learn to talk in phrases, no matter how enriched their environment, no matter or how great the love of their parents, no matter how much enthusiasm and ambition is expressed by their caretakers, and no matter how much native intelligence they possess. In the present chapter we will begin by generally reviewing the findings of Piaget, and conclude with a discussion of how recent studies have modified these ideas.

Piaget noted that cognitive and emotional development occur over a few major "periods" of childhood. The beginning and end of a period is not sudden, but gradual, and the periods merge one into the other. The qualitatively different operations of each period are not lost upon transition to the next level of development, but remain available throughout life to surface or whenever "higher," more sophisticated cognitive operations fail (for instance under the influence of drugs or alcohol, severe fatigue, or serious mental illness). In the Piagetian model, pivotal changes in cognitive capacity occur at three ages of childhood; 15 to 24 months, 7 to 8 years, and 11 to 13 years. These ages also may be cited as developmental landmarks in emotional development, which interdigitates with the Piagetian advances. In fact, the expected cognitive landmarks may be said to be dependent upon an assumption offered by Hartmann (1952) of an average expectable environment interacting with adequate biologic equipment for changes to occur.

Although the present chapter will focus primarily upon traditional Piagetian concepts, especially those which deal with changes at 7 and at 11 to 13, we will also take into account emotional factors. We believe these emotional changes to be very important when considering the various capacities of the developing child. Knowing that Piagetian and psychoanalytic theory do not always agree on specific developmental issues (see Basch, 1977), we still regard psychoanalytic theory as an important framework for understanding how a child uses various cognitive skills in emotionally tinged situations—the very same kinds of situations about which the law and society are so concerned.

## SENSORIMOTOR PERIOD

Although not particularly germane to issues of rights or questions of legal capacity, the young infant's and toddler's cognitive abilities prior to 15–24 months of age are important to this chapter, if only to contrast with subsequent stages, which do have legal implications. In the first year of life, children have an "internal" mental life manifested by a developing capacity to remember, recognize, and react in specific ways to both familiar and unfamiliar persons and objects. In contrast with the older child's ability to "think through" problems internally ("inside his head" so to speak), the infant's problem-solving behavior consists largely of "sensorimotor" solutions: motor manipulations done with the guidance of sensory feedback. Faced with a new situation, the very young child will try to master it by trial-and-error application of such sensorimotor schemes as are already present in his or her repertory. If the solution is possible with one such scheme, the child will be successful. If not, the child may go on trying until, by chance, happening upon an approach that works. This latter approach is likely to be incorporated into the baby's future problem-solving behaviors. The infant has now modified (through learning) the particular sensorimotor scheme in use. We have found no historical nor current legal milestone which takes ages 15–24 months into account, with the exception, perhaps, of adoption regulations. Two-year-olds are considered *older* children in adoption centers, thereby falling into the group for whom adoption by older or single parents and cross-racial adoptions are allowed. Attainment of object constancy is roughly parallel to the attainment of a representational reality in Piagetian terms (Mahler, Pine & Bergman, 1975). The concern with this latter concept and recent knowledge about attachment theory (Bowlby, 1972) have led to extended legal consideration of the psychological parent as a legitimate claimant on behalf of the child. As children begin to appreciate the reality of objects and things in their world, they also attain a stable mental attachment to significant caretakers. Disruptions of such bonds can interfere with and impede progress in cognitive and emotional development. Anna Freud's (1981) designation of the first 6 months of life as the period of "the need-satisfying object" felicitously informs us that taking care of the early infant's biological needs is soon superseded by later stages of psychological needs, which become more firmly ensconced as separation and individuation occur at 2 years.

## PERIOD OF CONCRETE OPERATIONS

Between the ages of 2 and 11 or 12 years, children slowly develop a repertory of "internal" cognitive operations of a "concrete" type, namely, operations concerned with manipulation of real things and ideas rather than purely hypothetical ones. Although Piaget initially conceived of this 10-year epoch as a single period, his observations soon forced him to divide the period into halves. Piaget termed the first half, extending from age 2 to our first landmark age, 6–7 years, the stage of "preoperational thought." He called the second, extending to age 11–12 (about 2 years short of our "magic" 14) the stage of "concrete operations."

The characteristics of "preoperational" logic have been described under a variety of terminologies in other psychological systems. The terminologies of neuropsychology and psychoanalysis are especially relevant here. In neuropsychology, preoperational thinking is "holistic" processing. In psychoanalytic metapsychology, the term "primary process thinking" carries with it many of the same attributes as Piaget's "preoperational thought." Similarly, the "concrete operations" of the older child (including "logical," cause-and-effect reasoning, the development of concrete classificatory schemes, and the use of algebraic-like reasoning chains) is similar to what is meant by "serial" or "sequential" operations in neuropsychology, and to what is called "secondary process thinking" in psychoanalysis (McLaughlin, 1978).

### Preoperational Thought

As White (1965) describes it, the very young child's thinking prior to age 6 or 7 tends to be primarily "associative" in nature. At about the time of entrance into the first academic grade, the child acquires the capacity to string together internal representations of stimulus-response-consequence into sequences that can be projected into the future, allowing planning, and into the past, allowing inference.

Central to the idea of preoperational thinking is the observation that preschool children cannot reason using cause-and-effect logic, but rather link ideas and classify phenomena because of accidental qualities and juxtapositions. For example, when asked "Why does the sun stay up in the sky?" some 4- or 5-year-olds might answer, with the unshakable conviction that their answer is correct, "Because it is hot (or round, or daytime, etc.)." This preschooler's own feelings are often passionately included in the reasoning processes. Because of the inability to use "later" "logical" cognitive operations to understand the phenomena noted in the everyday world, 4-year-old children's thinking may be replete with magical explanations. They may believe that their dreams are realities, that they take place in the room around them, and that dream figures may even come around to punish them because they have been bad. Yet at the same time, with structured questions they can say, "It's only make believe." They may "believe" they have the power to make the moon and clouds move (since they seem to do so when he walks outdoors) and also know that it is "only pretend." Many 4-year-olds already understand cause-and-effect logic and offer less personalized accounts. Recent research suggests that exposure to the types of questions and "practice," as well as individual differences in children, are important.

Beginning at around 5 or 6 years of age, young schoolchildren start to show evidence of a greater flexibility in their thinking, and of an ability to reason in a "proto-logical" manner. This new development marks the transition into the stage of concrete operations.

Emotional development, as reflected in psychodynamic psychology, parallels the stage-related framework we have outlined for a young child's cognitive development. Moving from oral to anal to oedipal stages the preschooler undergoes progressive emotional maturation. None of these important phases of "infantile sexuality" are marked by any particular logic of thought or concern about realities. By the time a youngster "resolves" his oedipal conflicts at age 5–7, he has developed a rudimentary conscience, has further refined his concern about how his behaviors affect others, and has developed a more objective way of defining his position in his family and at school. Thus, the completion of the three Freudian stages of infantile sexuality coincides perfectly with Piaget's timing for the beginning of "concrete operations"—age $7 \pm 1$ (Shapiro & Perry, 1976). With the passing of the oedipal stage, the child more completely attends to the sources of gratifications in terms of mother and father or their equivalents. These internalized stable constellations become potentially rigid structures that tinge developmental attainments with longings or fears attached to varying people in the world in what may become unrealistic unities. For example, the learning situation may be more felicitous for some if the instructor is male or female by virtue of prior experiences with parents.

Adults may retain a capacity to fantasy and to put together accounts of their experiences which do not follow the rules of logic, even though they already fully possess the capacity to understand logical cause and effect. The balanced use of fantasy and realistic thinking lends a certain creativity to otherwise dry mentation. Emotionally based thoughts tend to follow the rules of what might be called the "affective" (as opposed to the "cognitive" unconscious (Piaget, 1973).

## Concrete Operations

Mankind has almost universally recognized that at ages 6–8 children are ready to be taught. At $7 \pm 1$ children begin to be able to learn to think logically, to reason, and to use new reversible and flexible cognitive operations. They now have far more powerful tools than they did previously for understanding the world at large. Their duality of logical-illogical thinking gives school-age youngsters enhanced ability to use humor, a coping strategy which aids invaluably in dealing with stress and anxiety. By age 8 or 9 most children can be said to understand and internally manipulate cause-and-effect relationships between objects, events and situations.

Seven-year-olds demonstrate "social cognition." Though the scientific literature on the subject is somewhat incomplete (see Shantz,

1976), it appears that after age 7, children begin to understand that their own thoughts, feelings and intuitions can be the objects of another's thinking. Children of this age show the capacity to view the actions of others not solely in terms of the immediate effects, but also in terms of separate motivations. They begin to be able to infer the feelings of others.

Once children develop a capacity to carry out cognitive operations at a concrete level, the manner in which they view their interactions with the people around them may change. Around age 7 most youngsters further understand that parents (or other important persons in their life) can both love and punish at the same time, a realization that does not come at younger ages. Rather than dividing the world into those who are nice to him or her and those who are cruel or angry, the school-age child conceives more fully that people may simultaneously carry both good and bad intentions.

Yet, around age 8 or 9 years, the average child still exhibits certain rigidities in thinking, suggesting that he or she still views the world in relatively simplistic terms. This lack of mental flexibility reveals itself in the degree to which 1st, 2nd, and 3rd graders are not only rule conscious, but are unable to broaden their interpretations of the rules. This may lead the 7-, 8-, or 9-year-old to temporarily become more "religious" than his or her parents, or to act particularly argumentative (sometimes with reason) about parent's varying approaches to the "do's and don'ts." Youngsters during this period ask questions like "Why are you parking in a no parking zone, Daddy?" "Smoking is bad for you. All the commercials say so. So why do you keep smoking?" "Jimmy is only 6 months older than I am. Shouldn't he be allowed to stay up only 6 minutes later than I do." Children in the 2nd, 3rd, and 4th grades often set up clubs with such rigid and complicated rules that everyone spends their time debating the rules or nobody gets to join the club, let alone stay in. These phenomena suggest that the new inner controls on behavior of the 7- and 8-year-old are more rigid because the old, more primitive ways of thinking and the dangers of preschool emotionality are still quite real. The conscience as a mental structure is new to 7- and 8-year-olds, and it tends to take a harsh ungiving hold upon the child's attitudes and behaviors.

The process of developing concrete cognitive operations takes place over a period of years, and it may vary considerably from child to child. The process is one in which youngsters shift increasingly away from responses based on purely perceptual cues to ones based upon "logical" relationships, albeit on the concrete level.

By 10–12 years of age, children are more able to take the motives of others into account before they respond. They rely less upon talionic principles than do their 6-, 7-, or 8-year-old brothers and sisters. Because of the major role that cultural patterns, social mores, and familial beliefs play in a child's learning of morality, detailed schedules of age-related substages in the acquisition of "moral values" such as were given by Kohlberg (1964) have been sharply challenged. But most clinical observers of children note that the stronghold that the conscience establishes loosens considerably by ages 10–12, and that children develop far more flexible coping strategies by "late latency" than they employed at ages 6–7 when they were just entering the latency phase (Rest, Davison & Robbins, 1978). The variations in achievement of these changes from early childhood can best be exemplified by the effect on cognition of the emotional impact of disruption of average environments by divorce. Wallerstein and Kelly (1976) have documented the shift in concerns from the preoedipal child to the latency age child. While the younger child of divorce may seem selfishly concerned with getting things and security, the latency child may show guilt that he or she has been the cause of the disruption. The latter reaction attests to the role of irrational conscience and egocentrism. Although well-internalized guilt is an attainment for inner control, restraint and regulation, in settings of disruption emotional factors may turn the advance into a burden.

## PERIOD OF FORMAL OPERATIONS

"Formal operations," in Piaget's terminology, implies an ability to deal with the abstract, with the possible, and with what can be postulated. The onset of adolescence is marked by the acquisition of these abstract, powerful modes of thought. In the words of Neimark (1975), "The world of the adolescent is qualitatively different from the world of the child; it is far bigger, richer and more complex." Beginning around 11 or 12 years of age, children further understand such abstractions as metaphors and proverbs. They can formulate hypotheses, and they are able to devise creative "experiments" to test whether a hypothesis is correct or how it compares to other hypothesis. For the first time in their lives, youngsters begin to be able to understand probability and the laws of chance.

Formal operations, or formal thought, is obviously an ideal level of cognition—not one that can be equally achieved by all. Even those who learn how to abstract and to test hypotheses do not use these skills consistently or invariably. Different individuals may arrive at the same conclusion using entirely different methods of thinking. Thus, we may talk of "cognitive styles," and we are describing the processes, not the end points. The thinker may see the solution to a problem in a "flash" of insight, only to take months of careful analytical reasoning to prove that insight true. Differences in cognitive styles will strongly influence how one individual, as opposed to another, will observe and interpret events.

Lewis (1981) examined the degree to which 108 adolescents used formal or concrete operations in making their decisions. The youngsters ranged in age from 12 to 18 (grades 7 to 12) and were studied in simulated peer counseling situations. Each adolescent was presented with several dilemmas upon which his advice was needed by a hypothetical fellow-student. These problems included whether or not a peer should agree to a cosmetic surgical procedure, whether a peer should trust a research investigator about whom conflicting reports had come in, and how to decide on a surgical procedure about which two doctors disagreed. Lewis's results indicated that 7th, 8th and 10th graders (in comparison to 12th graders) tended to show relative lack of certain decision-making skills. These included deficiencies in: 1) imagining risks and future consequences; 2) recognizing the need for independent professional opinions; and 3) recognizing the potential vested interests of professionals when they provide advice. The 12th graders clearly had a greater capacity for these types of formal thought, though perhaps, as Dragastin and Elder (1975) have suggested, older adolescents really possess something closer to savvy than fully mature, formal thought. Lewis's study is the only one we have found which separates 14, our second historical milestone age, from 18, the current age of majority in the US, on the basis of a youngster's cognitive capacities. Clearly Piagetian formal thought begins to take shape a year or two before the milestone age of 14 is reached. All things considered, $14 \pm 1$ is quite a good landmark age for the expectation by society that children use abstract reasoning skills, and thus, that they be given increased responsibility.

## THE NEW PIAGET: A REAPPRAISAL OF SOME OLD IDEAS

For purposes of clarity, and because the ideas themselves remain clinically important, the above discussion focused primarily upon the "original Piaget." Increasingly during the past 2 decades, however, parts of the Piagetian system have been examined, picked apart, and reconstituted into a more mature package.

A reading of the third volume of the fourth edition of *Child Psychology* (Flavell & Markman, 1983) clearly demonstrates that few areas of the old Piagetian metapsychology have escaped scrutiny in the past 20 years. Some aspects of his system have withstood the test. There seems to be good cross-cultural validity to his findings, and children's cognitive strategies do become more-and-more complex and sophisticated with age. Also, children are not passive recipients of knowledge but have a very active role in the learning process, and the cognitive operations used by children during the sensorimotor stage are distinctly different in quality from those used by older children.

Most important, however, from the clinician's viewpoint, is the conclusion that the "qualitative" differences between stages may not be as marked as Piaget once thought. That is not to say that children faced with the familiar Piagetian tasks do not answer as the master said, but the idea that certain types of cognitive operations are only available in an absolute sense after certain ages is simply not true.

Children as young as 18 months of age have been shown to be capable of classifying objects differing on a single dimension (e.g., squares and circles), though more complex classification procedures may, as Piaget believed, not be learned until 10 or 11 years of age. Children as young as 3 or 4 years have been shown to be capable of solving various "conservation" problems, though the problems must be presented in relatively simple terms. Presented with cookies that vary in width and height, 4-year-old children can correctly assess the relationship between two dimensions and state which cookie is likely to be more desirable (because of its greater mass) to a hungry child.

Also, 3- and 4-year-old children may not be as "egocentric" as Piaget believed. Presented with the "three mountain" problem, the degree to which young children can assume the perspective of another viewer depends greatly on how familiar the child has become with the model and the manner in which he or she is questioned. Even at 30 months of age, in an analogous task, children who are asked to hold up a card may correctly state that an observer who is sitting opposite will see the design printed on the obverse of the card.

Children as early as 6 or 7 years demonstrate at least simple capacity to reason logically, a capacity which prefigures the more elaborated logical thought of the adolescent or the adult.

Based upon the newer research, then, certain basic ideas about the thinking and reasoning capacities of children and adolescents are consistent with the general description given by Piaget, but the underlying cognitive capacities themselves may be present, in at least nascent form, earlier than Piaget stated. Most importantly, we realize that such factors as individual differences between children and individual experience and opportunities to practice problem solving lead to a marked variability in children's performance in different contexts.

## STAGES OF EMOTION AND FANTASY

Many factors help the child develop a capacity to use secondary process thinking (Freud) or concrete and formal operations (Piaget). Piaget emphasized the importance of children's interactions with the environment, their constant attempts to solve a myriad of puzzling phenomena encountered in everyday life. Formal schooling is a second important factor Piaget stressed in the acquisition of formal thinking. Freud and his followers, on the other hand, stressed children's gradual development of more mature defense mechanisms, coping strategies, and sublimations as ways of becoming free of the domination of the pure drives and of primary process thinking. Ego maturation and development have been added, as the theory developed, to account for the emotional interface with experience in the world.

Fantasy, studied most by psychoanalysts and psychodynamic psychiatrists, is a crucial factor in the development of human thought. The Freudian theory of developmentally influential libidinal stages carries a central idea—that body (oral, anal, phallic, and genital) themes dominate children's mental processes during the early stages of development—that these early wishes organize the developing fantasy life in the same way that the Piagetian capacities for stages of "logic" gradually organize the human capacity to reason. The tendency of preschoolers to spend a good part of their mental energies wishing and personalizing caused Selma Fraiberg (1959) to call these very earliest moments in development "the magic years." By this, Fraiberg means that children under 4 or 6 cannot often break away from body-related fantasies and from extreme dependency upon caretaker(s).

All of this wish, compromise, and inner-directedness must be put aside, at least in part (the resolution of the oedipus conflict) before a youngster is free enough to enter the stage of latency (Freudian psychology) or the stage of concrete operations (Piaget) —both occurring at the magic age $7 \pm 1$.

We now come to the one place, a crucial place, indeed, that the Freudian and Piagetian schemes of development swing world's apart: adolescence. While Piaget notes the 14-year-old's cool capacity for reasoned logic, Anna Freud (1973) shows us that the adolescent suffers intense emotional assaults from burgeoning drives. The same type of wild assaults from inner-originating drives, fantasies, and fears that occurred during the oedipal phase of 4–5 occur again at the time of puberty. Youngsters are beset with sexual and aggressive urges, concerns about their own strange bodies, and fears of losing all control. At the very time that they begin to be able to abstract, adolescents cannot fully use these capacities because of the pressure of their own emotions. Small chance that an adolescent will write a book of formalistic thought while planning for a life of celibacy in order to fend off a vivid sexual dream experienced the night before.

This view of the tumultuous mental life of the 13–14-year-old is very important when the differences between 14 and 21 are considered. By 18, certainly by 21, we expect the emotional turmoil and bothersome intrusive fantasy life of adolescence to be somewhat resolved. It is, thus, the Freudian, not the Piagetian, view which provides us with the best scientific rationale for separating the ages of 14 and 21. Some data on adolescence indicates that the swings in emotion posited may not be as frequent or uniform in all individuals (Offer, 1969). Nonetheless we must be alert to the labile propensity of many adolescents.

## ASSESSING COGNITIVE AND EMOTIONAL DEVELOPMENT

IQ tests, within the limits of their interpretation, can inform us about a particular child's cognitive abilities and fund of knowledge. Knowing a child's age and IQ, and extrapolating this information to the child's likely stage of cognitive development, should permit us to judge whether the child may have a capacity to understand. Emotional and experiential factors, of course, futher influence the youngster's actual understanding of a given situation. Returning, however, to the question of children's potential for understanding, it has been noted that gifted children may attain the use of concrete or formal operations 1 or 2 years before their average counterparts

(Webb, 1974), while children whose intelligence is below average will achieve new Piagetian milestones at a slower rate (Inhelder, 1968). As would be expected, social and economic class levels also greatly influence the degree to which children will achieve new, more advanced cognitive operations. Almy, Chittenden and Miller (1966) and Peisach (1967) have demonstrated that a lower-class child may achieve "conservation" (i.e., an ability to understand that changes in shape or other characteristics of an object do not lead to changes in mass, weight, or volume) 1 year later than a middle-class counterpart.

For the clinician who wishes to conduct a more flexible, global assessment of the child's level (or stage) of cognition, new methods of doing so have been reported by Tanguay (1980). A good description of the domains Piaget studied and the tasks he used in his work can be found in the various editions of Flavel's textbook on Piaget's system, the first edition of which was published in 1964 and the last in 1973. Flavel's book is recommended for two reasons: It is a relatively simple and straightforward account of Piaget's theory, and it focuses on the clinically relevant aspects of the work. Having sought out and learned a representative sampling of the various "problems" Piaget used in questioning children, the clinician should keep certain key precepts in mind while assessing children. Piaget himself once said that the major error committed by most neophytes was to "talk too much, and inevitably suggest a particular answer to the child." Questions should always be posed in a neutral way, such as, "Is there more water, less water, or the same amount of water in this glass as compared to the other."

A second important precept is that it is not the child's actual answer which is sought, but the reasoning behind the answer. Keep asking, "How did you know that?" "Could you maybe explain it to me so I can understand?", etc. Raise hypotheses in your mind as to what may be going on in the child's mind, and devise ways to test whether they are true or false. *Play dumb;* it works wonders.

Thirdly, having gained as good an understanding of the child's reasoning as you can, find out how secure the child is in using the operation in question, or how close the child may be to learning to use the operation if he or she has not done so. "But look at how much higher (or lower) this surface is!" or "Look how wide the water is in this glass," you say to the child who has demonstrated the ability to conserve mass. Children who are not yet firm in their use of logical problem-solving tactics may waver in their judgment under such probing. Or they may waver because they see you as the authority figure; check this out as well. Lastly, an interpretation of the appropriateness of a particular child's performance will be greatly enhanced by the experimenter's experience in using this approach. With experience, the assessment becomes a series of games, suitable for informal insertion into play with the child.

The problem here, obviously, is: Do we take these wide differences in thinking abilities into account when we assess a child who has committed what in adult law would be a crime? Do we point up the slower development of formal thinking skills in the profoundly socially disadvantaged? Does society want to know?

## EMOTIONAL AND UNCONSCIOUS FACTORS

It is important from a legal viewpoint to recognize that a person's cognitive capacities may often be subject to distortion by internal fantasy and external stress. Test situations, such as intelligence assessments and school achievement evaluations, may give examiners some information about whether a child can arrive at a solution to a problem, but these tests alone will fail to reveal whether, under conditions of extreme emotional stress, a child was or will be able to reason at all. Thinking capacities are narrowly circumscribed to certain situations. Each Piagetian state of cognitive competence may be partly or completely compromised by difficult social and/or emotional circumstances. Conditions that dictate the need for a youthful court appearance (such as having been caught in a delinquent act, being fought-over in a custody proceding, or being called upon as a witness to an accident) involve strong emotions. These situations are highly charged because they threaten a youngster's security. They may involve psychic trauma, as well. They may also create stress because they call upon the child to use a newly gained critical faculty.

Strong emotions tend to stimulate fantasies in youngsters, making unconscious motivations increasingly important and causing the illogical to take precedence over the logical. As children approach adolescence, the degree to which they may display the expected "formal" maturity of thought may be influenced by tumultuous emotion, peer pressure, and family turmoil. Social coercion (the peer group) often dictates teenagers' behavior, despite the beautiful logic that they may regularly employ whenever they are calm enough and alone enough. Adolescence is clearly the time of life when emotional withdrawal from the family and movement toward the peer group may have a stronger influence on behavior than does the capacity to reason. These moves toward separateness and the distrust of those over 30 are nowhere better exemplified than in the unique languages that adolescents adopt and the music they prefer (Shapiro, 1985).

Developing drives, fantasies, and conscience guide children's behaviors and interfere with their thinking at different stages of their youth. External stress does the same. It is within the expertise of the child psychiatrist to integrate clinical examinations of a child with concepts of intelligence and of emotion in order to give courts, schools, and families a much more meaningful explanation of that particular child's capacities and actions than would any developmental timetables, or for that matter, any legally or historically designated ages.

## DISCUSSION

Although there is no question that we have been able to supply, through this developmental review, scientific bones and meat to society's choices of the ages of 7, 14, and 21 for many sorts of childhood rights and responsibilities, it is not our purpose to buttress what already has been done without proposing what might be done next or what could be done in the future, if we planned. Piaget, Freud, and their followers have shown us that by age $7 \pm 1$, an ordinary child can reason, albeit concretely, can hold some rudimentary moral values and ethics, and can function under guidance out in society without falling prey to temper tantrums, to fits of sexual display or to infantile clinging. Children a little above this age are almost automatically allowed into United States courts as witnesses in criminal trials and are held accountable for their own actions in US juvenile courts.

The problem is: Do we ordinarily see "ordinary" children in our courts? The socially deprived and chronically stressed youngster may not function at the Piagetian stage of concrete formal operations at age 7. The developmentally delayed and severely stressed child certainly does not. Nor does the mentally retarded youngster. What of the "latency" stage achievement, in Freudian terms? We know that children without fathers or mothers often take longer to complete oedipal development. We also know that there are early developmental delays in intellectually, psychologically, or socially disadvantaged children that preclude or delay their advancement into the relatively quiescent and intellectually productive period of latency. Certainly there are large numbers of children each year in the United States with good intellectual potential who are emotionally or psychologically unready for kindergarten, for reading, for writing, and for math. Are they ready for rights? For responsibilities?

Based upon what is known about development, we suggest that any child about whom there is a legally put question as to readiness for court, or for a court-administered punishment, be assessed first by a child psychiatrist serving as "friend of the court." There are too many variables to assume that an age makes for a development stage. Whenever questions of developmental stage come before our courts, ideally a child psychiatrist should be asked to apply these questions to the particular child.

Before statutes or school policies are set regarding children's age and stage, child psychiatrists must come before the bodies that consider such rules, or even better, they must consult at the onset with those who will propose the rules.

## REFERENCES

Almy, M., Chittenden, E., & Miller, P. (1966). *Young children's thinking: Studies of some aspects of Piaget's theory.* New York: Teacher's College Press.
Appleton, T., Clifton, R., & Goldberg, S. (1975). The development of behavioral

competence in infancy. In D. Horowitz (Ed.), *Review of child development research* (Vol. 4, pp. 101–186). Chicago: University of Chicago Press.

Basch, M.F. (1977). Developmental psychology and explanatory theory in psychoanalysis. *The Annual of Psychoanalysis, 5,* 229–263.

Bowlby, J. (1972). The nature of the child's tie to its mother. *International Journal of Psychoanalysis, 39,* 350–373.

Case, R. (1985). *Intellectual development: A systematic reinterpretation.* New York: Academic Press.

Dragastin, C., & Elder, G. (Eds.) (1975). *Adolescence in the life cycle.* Washington, DC: Hemisphere.

Fischer, K.W. (1980). A theory of cognitive development: The control and construction of hierarchies of skill. *Psychological Review, 87,* 477–531.

Flavell, J. (1973). *The developmental psychology of Jean Piaget.* Florence, KY: Van Nostrand Rheinhold.

Flavell, J.H. (1985). *Cognitive development.* Englewood Cliffs, NJ: Prentice-Hall.

Flavell, J.H., & Markman, E.M. (Eds.) (1983). Cognitive development. Vol. 3 in P.H. Mussen (Ed.), *Child psychology* (4th ed.). New York: John Wiley.

Fraiberg, S. (1959). *The magic years: Understanding and handling the problems of early childhood.* New York: Scribner.

Freud, A. (1966). *The ego and the mechanisms of defense.* New York: International Universities Press.

Freud, A. (1981). The widening scope of child psychology: Normal and abnormal: In *The writings of Anna Freud, 1970-80.* New York: International Universities Press.

Gardner, H. (1986). *The mind's new science.* New York: Basic Books.

Glick, J. (1975). Cognitive development in cross-cultural perspective. In D. Horowitz (Ed.), *Review of child developmental research* (Vol. 4, pp. 595–653). Chicago: University of Chicago Press.

Gruber, H. & Voneche, J. (1977). *The essential Piaget.* New York: Basic Books.

Haith, M., & Campos, J. (1977). Human infancy. *Annual Review of Psychology, 28,* 251–293.

Hartmann, H. (1952). The mutual influences in the development of ego and id. *The psychoanalytic study of the child* (Vol. 7, pp. 9–30).

Inhelder, B. (1968). *The diagnosis of reasoning in the mentally retarded.* New York: John Day.

Kohlberg, L. (1964). Development of moral character and moral ideology. In M.L. Hoffman & L.W. Hoffman (Eds.), *Review of child development research* (pp. 383–432). New York: Russell Sage.

Lewis, C.C. (1981). How adolescents approach decisions: Changes over grades seven to twelve and policy implications. *Child Development, 52,* 538–544.

Mahler, M., Pine, F., & Bergman, A. (1975). *The psychological birth of the human infant: Symbiosis and individuation.* New York: Basic Books.

McLaughlin, J.T. (1978). Primary and secondary process in the context of cerebral hemispheric specialization. *Psychoanalytic Quarterly, 47,* 237–266.

Neimark, E. (1975). Intellectual development during adolescence. In D. Horowitz (Ed.), *Review of child developmental research.* (Vol. 4, pp. 541–594). Chicago: University of Chicago Press.

Offer, D. (1969). *Adolescent turmoil. The psychological world of the teenager—A study of normal adolescent boys.* New York: Basic Books.

Peisach, E. (1967). The relationship between language usage and the achievement of conservation. *Dissertation Abstracts, 28* (6-13), 2612.

Piaget, J. (1973). The affective unconscious and the cognitive unconscious. *Journal of the American Psychiatric Association, 21,* 249-261.

Rest, J.R., Davison, M.L., & Robbins, S. (1978). Age trends in judging moral issues: A review of cross-sectional, longitudinal and sequential studies of the defining issues test. *Child Development, 49,* 263-279.

Shantz, C.U. (1976). The development of social cognition. In E.M. Hetherington (Ed.), *Review of child developmental research* (Vol. 5). New York: Russell Sage.

Shapiro, T. (1985). Adolescent language: Its use for diagnosis, group identity, values, and treatment. In S.C. Feinstein (Ed.), *Adolescent psychiatry, development and clinical studies* (Vol. 12, pp. 297-311). Chicago: University of Chicago Press.

Shapiro, T., & Perry, R. (1976). Latency revisited: The age of 7 ± 1. *The psychoanalytic study of the child,* (Vol. 31, pp. 79-100).

Siegler, R. (1986). *Children's thinking.* Englewood Cliffs, NJ: Prentice-Hall.

Sternberg, R.J. (1984). *Mechanisms of cognitive development.* New York: Freeman.

Tanguay, P.E. (1980). Cognitive development: Neuropsychology basis and clinical assessment. In L. Szymanski & P.E. Tanguay (Eds.), *Mental illness in mental retardation: Assessment, treatment, and consultation.* New York: University Park Press.

Wallerstein, J.S. & Kelly, J.B. (1976). The effects of parental divorce: Experiences of the preschool child. In S. Chess & A. Thomas (Eds.), *Annual progress in child psychiatry and child development* (Vol. 9, pp. 520-537). New York: Brunner/Mazel.

Webb, R.A. (1974). Concrete and formal operations in very bright 6- to 11-year-olds. *Human Development, 17,* 292-300.

White, S.H. (1965). Evidence for a hierarchical arrangement of learning processes. In L.P. Lipsitt & C.C. Spiker (Eds.), *Advances in child development and behavior* (Vol. 2). New York: Academic Press.

# 3

# IN THE NAME OF THE LAW

Questions of human rights and responsibilities and of personal accountability are fundamental issues which permeate the earliest writings of mankind. Along with procreation and family lineage, they are the subject about which the most ancient biblical writings speak, attesting to what men have always known to be the really important issues in life. In contrast to the first chapter, which peered back into the past, and the second, which took a glance sideways to review child development, this chapter will concentrate on contemporary law and give a general overview of current children's rights and responsibilities under the law. Criminal rights and responsibilities, money and contracts, and driving and drinking will be examined. Each area will be considered from the psychological perspective. We hope our concluding psychiatric commentary will open the subject to dialogue with the reader, hopefully by now an active participant in our "debate."

## CRIMINAL RIGHTS AND RESPONSIBILITIES

The law did not pay close attention to young lawbreakers as special cases until recent times. In 1899, in the humanitarian spirit of the age, the State of Illinois established the Juvenile Court of Cook County, the first to be designated exclusively for children's "crimes." The purpose was to remove the delinquent, neglected, and dependent child from the arena of adult proceedings, assignments of guilt and responsibility, and prisons. The child was to be protected, understood, guided, and, if necessary, placed in an improved home, adoptive or otherwise (*Laws of Illinois,* 1899). Because of this avant-garde move at the turn of the 20th century in America, our era came quickly to be known as the Century of the Child, and Chicago, as the birthplace of juvenile justice.

The age at which full criminal responsibility is assumed varies extremely, reflecting profound differences in cultures and epochs. Though psychologists might argue that an adult moral sense is possible by the age of 13 or 14, the legal age of responsibility in the United States is generally set at 16 to 18 years. Although not explicit, the relation of the individual to society and to the philo-sophical goals of the state seem to be the backdrop for the determi-nation of the age of responsibility.

In most states and in the federal courts, the judicial system treats as juveniles children under age 18. In New York, Connecticut, North Carolina, and Vermont, only those under 16 are so treated. In New York State, children aged 13–15 charged with serious crimes such as murder and arson may be tried in adult court without prior consideration of their cases by family court (*New York Times,* 1981).

In California, young men and women may be handled within the juvenile system until age 22. Many of these decisions are made early on a case-by-case basis by the judge conducting preliminary hearings. The judge may decide whether to hear the case in juvenile court or to remand the young person to trial in an adult criminal court. Even following an "adult" trial, a youth may be sentenced in California under the juvenile laws.

Denno (1979) reviewed the moral development and treatment potential of young people under the age of 18 and concluded that there is no justification for the abrupt distinctions between the ages of 10 and 16 in our various criminal responsibility laws. She felt that there is, instead, a very gradual transition from child-morality to adult-morality.

Binder-Arnold (1979), in a comprehensive review of the juvenile justice system, emphasized that attitudes and values regarding the "age of responsibility" have changed markedly over time and have differed greatly among cultures. Binder-Arnold also pointed out that the juvenile court system was originally based on the premise that children who violated criminal, behavioral, or ethical codes needed help, not punishment. The failure of the juvenile legal system to provide this kind of help in the form of guidance and treatment may have led to recent trends toward treating young perpetrators of crime as fully responsible.

In British law (McClean & Wood, 1969), children under 10 cannot be convicted of a criminal offense because they are presumed to lack the components of responsibility. Between the ages of 10 and 14, moral responsibility is established on an individual basis in England. After age 14, a child is assumed to be capable of full criminal responsibility. Imprisonment, however, is prohibited for persons under 17, and the imposition of imprisonment remains somewhat restricted for those between 17 and 21. Young offenders, thus, come under a dual system in England: criminal jurisdiction for the guilt-innocence determination and civil jurisdiction upon sentencing. In England the convicted juvenile is believed to require care, protection, or control. Goodman (1970) notes that in England "informal police caution" (in which youths, and possibly their parents, would be called in and warned of the consequences of their actions) has been given uniformity and statutory emphasis, the objective being to keep the juvenile out of court.

Amir-Menachem (1966) states that in Israel, 9 years of age is the minimum age for criminal responsibility. Many factors beyond age are considered before prosecution of a child can be brought. For example, the police must certify that a given case cannot be handled by the parents, teachers, or other involved adults. The seriousness of the crime is also taken into account when dealing with a young offender.

In the Soviet Union (Morozov & Kalashnik, 1970), criminal proceedings cannot be instituted if a child has not yet attained the age of 14. From 14 to 16, three specific crimes are set aside for adult responsibility: murder, deliberate infliction of bodily harm, and rape. From 16 to 18, any crime can be prosecuted in adult court, and if convicted, a youthful offender must serve time in a special correctional labor colony. Organic brain disorders are the only factors that can exculpate a crime committed by a young Soviet citizen over age 16–18.

Because young children often steal, and begin doing so at quite young ages, the laws regarding theft have been less strict (though encompassing younger ages) than statutes dealing with direct harm to others. The law has generally assumed that there is no criminal intent in thefts committed before age 7, though this age has been pushed upward in some jurisdictions: to 8 in England, 9 in Texas, 10 in Georgia, and 12 in Arkansas. These laws are difficult to enforce because it is hard to establish that children who steal are motivated by complex understanding of the act. Regardless of peer pressures or their basic sense of self-esteem or identity, young offenders must know that the items they took were not theirs, and that it was wrong for them to take them, and they must fully understand the consequences of their actions and thus, be "accountable" for their acts in order to be held criminally. These legal requirements for responsibility for theft are not particularly easy for prosecutions to meet.

## Discussion

Recent trends in the handling of juvenile offenders concern us. The decrease in the age of responsibility and the remanding of 15–17 year olds into adult criminal courts implies a profound pessimism on the part of society about ever rehabilitating the juvenile offender. Since the Gault decision, an early 1960s US Supreme Court case, which enabled any juvenile accused of a crime to receive a full legal defense, great amounts of money have been poured into enabling youngsters to have their own attorneys on their day in court. But there has been no echoing outpouring of funds toward rehabilitative efforts for convicted juveniles.

We know more now about rehabilitation for drug users and alcohol abusers than we knew 20 years ago. We also have more options of brief psychotherapies, treatments with medication, and group work with adolescents than we had previously. But the facilities for the criminally convicted juvenile have not kept pace with our knowledge. Money has not flowed and our legislatures have not been interested in our therapeutic "know-how." In some ways, whether the young offender goes to adult prison or to an outdated juvenile correctional facility may not actually matter much today, that is, if no treatment is offered or if none is even available.

There are, of course, some individuals whose early experience has been so flawed that even our best efforts can do little to prevent their engaging in criminal acts by age 13–15; more crime will be inevitable. But there are other adolescents—far more numerous than those who are hopeless—who, if given adequate intervention using behavioral modification, group therapy, vocational rehabilitation, education, and insight, could modify their actions and go on to reasonably productive, noncriminal lives. The young certainly deserve this chance.

If a young person has already had an opportunity to go for treatment to the type of therapeutic facility outlined above and then proceeds to commit another serious crime, there would be considerable question as to whether expensive rehabilitative efforts should once more be applied. We cannot in any way predict criminality, but some mechanism to prevent useless expenditure of funds would be useful. Perhaps some offenders would be helped by being given a "second chance" or even a "third chance," but to do so for everyone risks sinking the entire rehabilitation enterprise through excessive costs. We believe that young persons should at least be given one chance. If they fail, remands into the adult system, unless mitigating circumstances can be proven by the adolescent, may be in order. We cannot ask society to "bet" on the highest risk adolescents just because we believe in children.

## PROPERTY RIGHTS OF CHILDREN

The ownership and transfer of real and personal property relates psychologically to certain emotional and cognitive tasks of development: differentiation of the self from others, manipulation and quantification of objects, appreciation of things unseen, and consideration of the complex consequences of behavior. Through their actions and interaction with others, children come to learn the concepts "mine" and "not mine." Eventually, money is seen by youngsters to carry value and power. The cognitive understanding required to manipulate more abstract, unseen financial properties (futures, bonds, or stocks) requires the use of higher level formal thinking operations, a related education, and the capacity to endure delay, reversals, and frustration.

The attitude of the law regarding property owned by juveniles has been arbitrary, though the law has recently acquired a bit more flexibility. The law divides all property into real property (land) and personal property (all the rest, including money, stocks, bonds and personal possessions). The capacity of a minor to make a contract to dispose of or to exchange property is not the same as an adult's capacity; that is, the contract of a minor (in most states, a person under eighteen) may be invalid. Minors are assumed by the law to be unable to protect themselves from unscrupulous dealings. In practice, however, a child alone, or a parent acting as the guardian, frequently will dispose of property belonging to the child, particularly if it is personal property of no great value, without legal interferences. If the child handles the disposal of the property, the transfer may be revocable, although if the remuneration for the item is reasonable, current courtroom trends would tend toward letting the contract stand. In other words, there is increasing recognition that in some instances a minor has the capacity to make a binding contract. The American Bar Association has recommended legislation that would allow contracts made by persons over age 12 to be binding.

## Discussion

The idea that 12-year-olds, the vanguard of whom have just recently come into the stage of formal operations, could ordinarily understand the abstractions involved in property tax, future valuation, and investment income is seriously flawed. No 12-year-old could stand on his or her own in contract making, and the trend toward allowing them to do so is without any psychological foundation.

We are just recently coming out of a phase in US history in which late adolescents and young adults gave up huge tracts of land and personal income to gurus, cults, friends, and charlatans. We realize from sad experience that even 18 is not a good age at which contracts should be binding. Young love—be it for a person or for a group—can be blind. Twenty-one, the upper age limit of majority (for drinking, for example), is the most appropriate age—except in individual cases that can be pleaded first in court—for entering into binding contracts without the cosignature of a guardian. In the instance of contracts, age 21 seems most appropriate. As the general age at which the storms of adolescence are quiet enough to allow reasonably mature interactions with others, 21 appears to be an acceptable age for dealing alone with personal property.

On the other hand, where a will automatically provides that an estate will go to offspring at majority, considerations of maturity ought to take precedence over age. This sometimes does not occur until ages 30–35. The vicissitudes of young love, divorce, career experimentation, lifestyle consideration, and educational forays within the 20- to 30-year-old group suggest that the fourth decade of life would be a more appropriate starting point for personal management of major inheritances than the third.

## DRIVING AND DRINKING

In the United States in the first half of the 20th century, age 21 was the legal age for purchasing and drinking alcohol. When, in more recent years, the age of majority was lowered to 18, some states permitted drinking at 18 and others held fast at 21.

The laws regarding drinking and, to a lesser extent, driving reflect society's resolution of the conflict between the wish to accord a person a right ("If he's old enough to fight in Viet Nam, then why isn't he old enough to drink?") and the facts: Motor vehicle accidents kill more people in the 15- to 24-year-old age group than the next five causes of death combined. Many of these automobile-related teenage and young adult deaths (as is true for car accidents caused by more "mature" adults) are alcohol related. Although studies (National Safety Council, 1981) have shown that raising the drinking age can be effective in reducing the incidence of teenage automobile accidents and death, there are some who oppose passage of these laws. More federal highway money has been recently made available to states with a drinking age of 21, so many states have raised the age to 21.

Imposing severe punishments for alcohol impaired drivers, such as mandatory license suspension or jail sentences, has also been successful in decreasing alcohol-related deaths, but only when the public perceives punishment to be certain and swift (NHTSA, 1980–81). The British Road Safety Act of 1967 initially reduced the percentage of alcohol-related road fatalities by 40%, but when it became clear in subsequent years that enforcement of the penalties was lax, the number of alcohol-related fatalities rose until it exceeded what it had been prior to passage of the act. In America, mandatory license suspension and jail sentences for drunk drivers appear to have resulted in increased plea-bargaining, court backlogs, and decreased conviction rates (Insurance Institute for Highway Safety, 1981).

There is some evidence that raising the minimal age for buying liquor decreases driving accidents and deaths. A 1982 *New York Times* editorial stated: "The point here can't be repeated too often: Laws that limit teenage drinking don't just protect young people from themselves. They protect everyone on the road."

## Discussion

We concur with the recent trends toward a uniform drinking age of 21 in all states. Alcoholism in teenagers appears to increasing. It is not inappropriate to require that early maturing adolescents wait until their less mature "brothers" have grown older before each can be given their drinking rights. Adolescent drinking often is a communal act, and if everyone is forbidden to do so up to 21, we may begin to limit the tragic effects of drinking and driving in adolescence.

## RELIGIOUS ISSUES

Traditionally it has been the parents' right, and often their perceived obligation, to determine their children's religious practices until the age of majority or emancipation. On the other hand, when children are able to reason on an abstract level, beginning at about 11 or 12, religious exploration or religious "rebellion" may occur. Religious differences between parents and children may result in a conflict between the parents' traditional expectations and rights to make religious choices for their children and the youngsters' gathering personal rights—especially as they get older—to self-determination. In many instances, states have claimed that their interest in the child's welfare outweighs the parents' rights to determine their child's religious practices. Examples of this type of state intervention into the parent-child relationship include one state's prohibition of proselytizing by minors, and other states' demands that the religious beliefs of the parents or guardians be put aside when they interfere with a child receiving a needed type of medical care. At times, however, parental rights have been upheld. In *Wisconsin v. Yoder* (1974), an Amish group was allowed to withhold their children from public school as a matter intrinsic to their free exercise of religion. The parents' right to guide their children as they pleased was held to outweigh the state's general interest in the education of its citizens or the youngsters' potential for development in secular schools.

The surge of interest in the 1960s and 1970s in new or "cult" religions alarmed many American parents of adolescents and young adults. Because adolescence is a time of profound change, conflicts between conformity and individuality and dependence and independence may render the young person vulnerable to religious conversion and even to complete personal "takeover" and "makeover." Young people may choose religion as their personal battleground if they know this to be a sensitive issue for the family. Cults have tended to attract youths with previous behavioral disturbances (Deutsch, 1975; Galanter et al., 1979) and/or those who have already failed at school, at work or in relationships. Some groups have used sophisticated, sometimes harsh, behavioral techniques, which tend to set their new acolytes' conversions quite firmly (Delgado, 1977; Sargent, 1957). Once in such a group, whether the reinforcement for staying is kindly or harsh, a young convert is likely to stay.

Delgado (1977) states that parents of minors (under 18 years old in most states) have a legal right to custody of their children, but in reality, it may be difficult to enforce custody of a minor who has become a cult group member. If the cult life is harmful to the minor, as Delgado and others (Singer, 1979) believe, the parents may be able to assert their rights of custody. Delgado has proposed model legislation which would protect children, especially when it can be proven that they were being held separate from society-at-large and were being harmed. This model legislation provides that the child spend a legally enforced period of time away from the cult and be reexposed to society-at-large. An eventual decision on the part of the minor as to whether he or she wished to rejoin the cult or to remain outside would be required.

## Discussion

Based upon our review of the issues, we believe that parents do not have an absolute right to make life-and-death decisions for their children based solely upon religious belief. We believe that this is as true for a teenager as for an infant. Few would disagree that children in need of a lifesaving transfusion should have the opportunity to petition the court to receive a transfusion despite the religious wishes of their parents. But we also think it reasonable that children be able (directly or through their advocate) to present a case to court in regard to other important issues, such as that of school attendance. If a child wishes to attend school, but the parent's religious beliefs preclude this, the parent's decision should not necessarily be final.

We also note that parents commonly determine the religion of their child. Divorced parents may argue the point, each wishing the child to be raised under a different set of rituals. This is especially true when a child is coerced to submit to one set of beliefs in one home and to an entirely conflicting set in the other. When the parents each feel very strongly about the issue, and when they each demand allegiance to their religion, the child may feel guilty, anxious, and confused. In religious matters, as in other areas of interparental disagreement, it is the conflict itself and the attempts at coercion that harm the child. In custody battles, the child psychiatrist can assist the court in better understanding the emotional and interpersonal conflicts which the child may be experiencing around such issues. When there is extreme religious coercion by divorced parents who have joint legal custody, the courts may need to determine who should have physical custody of the child.

The choice of religion does not often become an issue in court or in the psychiatric clinic. Recently, however, some families have become extremely upset when their teenage (or early college-age) son or daughter elected to joint a religious cult. "Was he or she coerced?" they ask. "Will he or she be harmed by cult beliefs?" Their concern may be legitimate. Children may need time to mature, emotionally and cognitively, before they can fully organize their religious beliefs. Membership in a rigid and all-encompassing social system, as may be found in some cults, could prevent this maturation from taking place. Parents have attempted to "rescue" offspring from a cult, and the matter has ended in court. An examination of both the parents and the teenager or young adult by a child psychiatrist may help the court decide what is best for the young person.

## SEXUAL AND FAMILY ISSUES

The family is traditionally the unit that transmits the values of society to the next generation. But in this era of civil rights and increased individual choice, the trend of court decisions in the United States has often been toward the rights of the individual as apart from those of the family. The courts and legislative bodies may have the power to determine at what age an individual may decide independently to marry, to obtain contraceptives, to have an abortion, or to give up a child for adoption, but judges and lawmakers alone cannot deal with the complex interpersonal and developmental issues involved in adolescent and childhood sexuality. A state may legislate, but it is still the primary responsibility of the family to help the minor child reach reasonable decisions.

A clear succession of American court decisions has nonetheless supported the concept that adolescents (often lumped together into a single age group from 12 to 18) have the same basic civil and constitutional rights as adults when it comes to their sexual expression. Perhaps the most hotly contested issue today is the right to seek an abortion. A United States Supreme Court decision, *Belotti v. Baird* (1979), directly confronted the issue of whether a minor female capable of becoming pregnant can independently decide whether she may undergo an abortion. The court stated that, under certain circumstances, a minor female does not need parental consent nor is she under any obligation to inform her parents of her decision to seek and obtain an abortion. This decision concluded a long series of abortion cases, beginning with the landmark *Roe v. Wade* (1973) decision, which had struck down a state anti-abortion statute 6 years earlier.

In cases involving abortion and contraception, courts have gradually extended the rights of privacy from married adults to unmarried minors. Recent cases involving minors show, however, that the Supreme Court is deeply divided over the relative power to be distributed within the family, between children on the one hand and parents on the other (Guyer, 1981). The split is a reflection of the underlying disagreements among the justices about the proper balance between individual freedoms and parents' right to control the behavior and conduct of their own children. The legal debate appears to center upon just where, not whether, a line should be drawn between parents and their youngsters.

Through legal decree, rights can be bestowed as a kind of "birthday gift," namely, a right bestowed upon a child by virtue of reaching a particular age. Legal rights arbitrarily assigned by age, however, may raise more problems than are solved unless the chosen chronological age does, in fact, coincide with the age at which the youngster is likely to have achieved adequate decision-making capacities to exercise the right in question.

## Discussion

We believe in the importance of full communication within families. Whenever possible, children and their parents should mutually make decisions regarding contraception, abortion, adoption, and future parenthood. But for most adolescents, these are the very issues that are most difficult to discuss with others, and especially with their parents. These are issues that tend to be kept to the self, or to be shared only with peers.

From early in puberty, at times even before the first menstrual period or nocturnal emission, the "child" may be fertile. As the age of menarche currently moves down from 13 or 14 to 11 or 12, the capacity for making wise judgments has not moved downward in a like way. Moreover, the emotional end of adolescence appears to be moving up the chronological scale. This is manifested by teenagers' continuing financial dependence on their parents and delay in entering the workforce. Thus, youngsters are left in a mental and emotional no man's land between the ages of 12 and 22; they are physically mature, but emotionally and intellectually unformed. The sexual revolution of the 1960s has added to this problem. Sex is fully available, yet the capacity for reason and emotional control evades many of our adolescents.

There appears to be a slightly more conservative trend among teenagers in the late 1980s regarding their sexual activity. Perhaps the recent herpes epidemics and the AIDS scourge may force youngsters to reconsider their sexual behaviors during this enormously difficult period of desynchronization between full physical and mental maturity. Former eras were equally beset by the threat of other venereal infections, however, without such possibilities leading necessarily to safer sexual behaviors, even among adults.

We believe that contraceptive clinics should be available free of charge to all adolescents in the United States. Certainly the human price of raising unwanted or unclaimed children far exceeds the price of providing birth control devices to teenagers. There are some who feel that the availability of birth control may serve as an encouragement to early sexual activity. We believe that the issue is responsible sexuality, not early sexuality. Peer group pressure is a far greater encouragement to early sexuality than would be the availability of any contraceptive. The larger question is how to influence adolescent peer groups so that they act in more responsible ways. Recently, in several school districts in the United States, health clinics have been set up to offer education to male and female students regarding important sexual issues, including AIDS and contraception. We believe that this approach should be strongly encouraged as an effective solution to some of the most serious problems facing teenagers today.

## REFERENCES

Amir-Menachem, (1966). *Project follow-up summary: Delinquent behavior of children below the age of criminal responsibility.* Jerusalem: Ministry of Social Welfare.

*Belotti v. Baird,* 443 US 622, 1979.

Binder-Arnold, A. (1979). The juvenile justice system: Where pretense and reality crash. *American Behavioral Scientist, 22,* 621–652.

Delgado, R. (1977). Religious totalism: Gentle and ungentle persuasion under the first amendment. *Southern California Law Review, 51,* 1–98.

Denno, D. (1979). Moral development and treatment potential of youths under age 18. *Adolescence, 14,* 399–409.

Deutsch, A. (1975). Observations on a sidewalk ashram. *Archives of General Psychiatry, 32,* 166–175.

Galanter, M., Rabkin, R., Rabkin, J., & Deutsch, A. (1979). The "Moonies": A psychological study of conversion and membership in a contemporary religious sect. *American Journal of Psychiatry, 136,* 165–170.

In re Gault, 87S. 875 CT 1428, US Supreme Court.

Goodman, L. (1970). English juvenile courts: Recent changes in legislation. *International Journal of Offender Therapy, 14,* 105–110.

Guyer, M. (1981). *Personal communication.*

Insurance Institute for Highway Safety. (1981). *Drinking-driving laws; What works?* Status Report 16:1.

*Laws of Illinois,* 1899, p. 131.

McClean, J.D., & Wood, J.C. (1969). Young offenders. In J. McClean (Ed.), *Criminal justice and the treatment of offenders* (pp. 175–257). London: Sweet & Maxwell.

Morozov, G.V., & Kalashnik, I.M. (1970). *Forensic psychiatry.* New York: International Arts and Science Press.

National Safety Council (1981). *Accident facts.* Chicago: NSC.

*New York Times,* April 1981, July 24, 1981.

*New York Times,* February 14, 1982, p. 20EY.

NHTSA. (1980–81). *Alcohol and safety. NHTSA, Workshop Series,* p. 45.

*Roe v. Wade,* 410 US 113, 1973.

Sargent, W. (1957). *Battle for the mind: A physiology of conversion and brain washing.* New York: Doubleday.

Singer, M.T. (1979, January). Coming out of the cults. *Psychology Today.*

*Wisconsin v. Yoder* 406 US 205, 1974.

# 4

## CONSENT, ASSENT, AND DISSENT: CHILDREN IN TREATMENT AND RESEARCH

Within the past decades, there has been increasing interest in the subject of children's rights in regard to hospitalization and research. Laws that limit the degree to which adults may be hospitalized against their will or that mandate more explicit informed consent for research subjects have been implemented within the United States. However, it has not been entirely clear how these guidelines are meant to be applied to children and adolescents, although there has been a general consensus that the subject is an important one. It is difficult to achieve a balance between the current needs of society to protect its members and its future needs to prevent disease. Furthermore, there are huge potential conflicts between the rights of parents, the rights of an individual child, and the rights of the public in the treatment-research areas. These conflicts not only engender passionate arguments, but also lead to extremes of opinion and even political campaign rhetoric. This chapter will address these issues, focusing primarily upon childhood "informed" consent.

Consent is the legally required declaration by the subject (or guardians if the subject is incapacitated or a minor) to agree to treatment or to participate in research. Assent, which is not a legal term, is the approximation of consent and implies that the child agrees to participation within his or her capacity to understand. Dissent is an active disagreement to participate, expressed either verbally or nonverbally. As Cooke (1977) has stated, it is generally agreed that consent serves three functions: to provide protection against harm, to recognize the autonomy of the subject, and to honor the dignity of the individual. Even in the case of adults, consent may not be informed, though it often can be said to be educated (Inglefinger, 1972).

Any discussion of informed consent must keep in mind that different situations may call for very different levels of concern. People are not usually concerned when treatment is routine, non-experimental, and uses generally accepted techniques. It is the new and the unusual which arouses concern.

*A Case Vignette.* Roger was a 38-month-old boy when first seen by a child psychiatrist. His parents already knew that he was retarded. They brought him for examination in order to reach some decisions regarding their role in Roger's future. The central question was whether Roger should be institutionalized. He was much harder to manage at home than were his older siblings, he was obviously already behind in many aspects of his development, and the parents, particularly the mother, were pessimistic and depressed about him. Both sets of grandparents were also involved in the decision regarding institutionalization, the maternal grandparents feeling the child should be institutionalized, and the paternal grandparents believing that he should be kept at home. In a family session, Roger appeared to be an attractive child, who related well to the examiner. He had speech, though it was delayed, and he was poorly coordinated. The psychiatrist recommended that Roger remain at home and reviewed with the parents various community supports that would be available to the family if they, themselves, raised Roger. The family resolved to keep the child inside the family unit.

Thirteen years later the parents again consulted the child psychiatrist. They had decided that Roger should have a vasectomy for his own and for the family's protection. They described Roger as a handsome, outgoing, cheerful, but very childish 16-year-old. He liked people and trusted them, but his parents feared that he might be easily manipulated or exploited. They wanted to be sure, they said, that he would not impregnate a partner. Roger had schooling in special classes, and he had begun working part-time in his father's small retail business, sweeping the floor, moving merchandise, etc. Roger was seen by the psychiatrist and was, indeed, a

handsome, well-developed, and engaging 16-year-old. He
was friendly, poised, and reasonably sure of himself. He was
polite and showed considerable evidence of the loving and
structured parenting and training he had received. His mental age was estimated at about the 5-year level.

A urologist had refused to perform a vasectomy upon
Roger without an order from the juvenile court, yet the court
refused to give its consent without a psychiatric opinion.
Roger, himself, was certainly of the chronological age at which
a personal consent would have been mandatory. But what of
his mental age? Can a 5-year-old really make such a life-
effecting decision for himself?

The child psychiatrist, after weighing and discussing with
the parents the various aspects of Roger's rights and capacity
for responsibility, as well as the parents' responsibility, recommended to the court that the vasectomy appeared to be in the
best interest of society, and also of the parents and the child,
since both could suffer should Roger impregnate someone.
The court gave its approval and Roger had the operation.

Another kind of public concern comes up when an older child's
treatment includes psychiatric hospitalization; even greater concern is expressed if the treatment to be utilized is experimental in
nature, even if the child is likely to benefit from the new treatment.
The greatest public concern becomes manifest when a child is
asked to undergo a research procedure which may only benefit
future children. The ethical questions inherent in each of these
three issues—hospitalization, new methods of treatment, and future-
directed research studies—are very different. The dilemmas are
being resolved (by public opinion and the courts) in diverse ways.
We are far from any consensus or routine, however. This chapter
will address these three issues, and will conclude with some general comments about safeguarding the rights of children.

## INVOLUNTARY PSYCHIATRIC HOSPITALIZATION

*A Case Vignette.* A 13-year-old boy was admitted to the neurological unit of a large city hospital for an evaluation of a
suspected central nervous system disorder. He had a 2-3-year

history of truancy, lying, arson, drug dealing, and running away. The neurological work-up was negative. A psychiatric consultant diagnosed conduct disorder, socialized and agressive type. Due to the severity of the problem, psychiatric hospitalization was recommended for the boy. The parents would not give their formal consent, but said they did not care what was done to him. They did not want their son returned home.

The boy made an impassioned plea to the hospital staff that he was old enough to be "let free" to make his way in the world. A reluctant and apprehensive staff decided, with the approval of the parents, to discharge him, agreeing to let him assume responsibility for himself. After a 10-month odyssey of odd jobs, traveling, living with concerned families, and "bumming around," the boy decided to return home. He had discovered that it was hard to get work at 13, that one could get arrested for hitchhiking, and that having no home address created many problems. The parents agreed to have him back if he stopped his antisocial behavior. When last heard from, the young man reported no further conflict with society. He was enrolled in graduate school. While the drastic approach taken by the staff in releasing a 13-year-old to be on his own might not be considered safe, in some rare instances unusual approaches can work.

As is true of other "rights of children," the right to refuse psychiatric treatment is relatively new. Until the mid-1960s, parents had the sole discretion to hospitalize or to remove from the hospital against medical advice any child under 18, and in some states even under 21. Only if the action were blatantly inappropriate would the medical authorities intercede against the parents' wishes and try to persuade a court to countermand the parents' intent in the matter of admission or discharge. Political pressures of all kinds might be brought to bear if the minor child came from an influential family.

There are certainly times when it is not only in the best interest of the child that he or she receive psychiatric treatment, but in the interest of the state to ensure that such therapy is provided. When a youngster is dangerous, the state's interests certainly rest with confining the child and providing that child with treatment. Both moral and economical considerations argue that whenever possible, treatment be delivered in a manner that is least restrictive, such as on an outpatient basis or on an unlocked ward. If inpatient treatment is necessary, parents must be involved in discussions concerning the child's admission to the psychiatric hospital and they should assume responsibility for the decisions made regarding their youngster. But parents may not always act in the best interest of the child. They, too, have vested interests. If parents hire an attorney, this professional will represent the parents' position. Oftentimes, however, the attorney for the parents will fail to put before the court the child's needs, wishes, or status.

To complicate the situation further, a disturbed young child or adolescent cannot be trusted to act in his or her own best interests, at least as the rest of society would define these interests.

> *A Case Vignette.* An 8-year-old fell off a parapet, severely disfiguring her face. This occurred around Easter after weeks during which she had frightened the nuns at her school by planning a reunion with her dead mother. The child did not "recognize" the unconscious suicidal wishes behind her "accident," but fortunately for her, the nuns, the grandparents and the psychiatrist did. She was signed into the hospital by her guardians, the grandparents, against her will. She remained there for three weeks, after which she was seen for an extended period for weekly psychotherapy, during which time she became symptom free. She has remained so for several years.

The "acting out" of unconscious conflicts, as noted in this clinical example, is a hallmark of the stage that follows latency, adolescence, as is the denial of dependency needs. The adolescent struggle for emancipation and independence often precludes recognition of a need for psychotherapy. Teenagers' valuation of their freedoms and their tenuous sense of identity may be threatened by the idea of hospitalization, leading to the view that hospitalization must be resisted to the bitter end.

It seems reasonable that teenagers should, during involuntary commitment hearings, be allowed the same safeguards granted to adults, and that from age 13 or 14 *voluntary* admission be allowed on the patient's (but no one else's ) request. Although the hearings, safeguards, and attorneys for mid-adolescents may be the same as for adults, the treatment programs for adolescents cannot be identical to those for adults. Adolescents require social (peer relations) and educational programs (inhospital schooling) which cannot be administered adequately when adults and adolescents are housed and treated together on the same wards. Treatment is the quid pro quo for society's right to act in parens patriae. For treatment to be truly therapeutic, it must be appropriate to the developmental as well as to the psychological needs of the patient, and the particular demands of his or her illness.

Schowalter (1978) points out that issues of minors' rights regarding outpatient psychiatric treatment usually focus less on parental coercion than on minors' ability to seek their own therapy without the knowledge or consent of the parents. Schowalter suggests that the child psychiatrist has an option: He or she may, on request, give outpatient treatment to a minor who understands and gives consent but who has not informed his or her parents. If the psychiatrist does decide to take such a child into treatment, one goal might be to aid the patient in understanding that optimal therapy would require the knowledge of and/or participation in therapy by the parents. A self-referred minor would be responsible for payment of fees for services. The child psychiatrist taking on such a case would have to document fully the young patient's degree of understanding at the time that the therapeutic alliance was made, the nature of the child's agreement to the proposed treatment, and the therapist's reasons for proposing this form of therapy.

## RISKS OF PSYCHIATRIC HOSPITALIZATION

There are a number of risks inherent in psychiatric hospitalization of children, whether the hospitalization is voluntary or involuntary. All of us recognize that there may be serious physical risks which accompany certain treatment procedures (most notably, aversive conditioning and pharmacotherapy). The risks of long-standing mental disease, however, are usually much greater than those connected with treatment. There is a stigma connected with psychiatric hospitalization, and this may remain with a child long after discharge from the institution. The losses and gains in this regard must also be considered. While much of the public no longer equates a child's outpatient psychotherapy with that child being "crazy," inpatient treatment is still regarded as proof of "nuttiness," "flakiness," or "going bonkers." No longer is mental illness hidden in euphemisms like "nervous breakdown" or "mental and physical exhaustion." Instead, the public tends to equate all psychiatric hospitalization with psychosis. (We have already shown in a previous clinical vignette of this chapter—the girl who fell and "broke" her face—that a hospital stay may come about on a very different basis). If one were to choose between the stigma of incarceration in a juvenile detention facility and the stigma of commitment to a psychiatric institution, the stigma of the former would probably be less damaging. In many states a child's juvenile record is destroyed or "sealed" when that juvenile reaches age 18. Not so for the records of a juvenile psychiatric hospitalization. Most choices, however, are for hospitalization, because a hospital would be far more likely to be treatment oriented than would be a detention home.

There is not likely to be considerable disagreement among doctor, child patient, and parents about the need for inpatient treatment when a youngster is suffering from an acute psychotic reaction or from a severe suicidal depression. The youngster may object, but can usually be persuaded, and will most often demonstrate sizable relief upon entering the hospital.

There may be less agreement between doctor, child patient, and parents if the hospitalization has been recommended because of the child's violent behavior. The parents may be afraid of the eventual consequences to themselves if they force their frightening child into the hospital involuntarily, yet they are caught in a bind between leaving their youngster "on the street" and incurring the child's wrath. The psychiatrist, as well as the parents, may incur threats or actual attacks from the child patient. Interestingly, the child can be, in part, an ally in these instances. There is a distinct possibility that the child fears his or her own anger. The child may refuse and fight admission, but feel considerable relief upon finding him- or herself in the hospital nonetheless.

The underlying question about enforced treatment against a child's will is: How can the doctor carry out responsibilities without adequate authority from the state, the parents, or the child? Parents remain responsible for their offspring until they reach the age of 18, but their legal authority over youngsters has gradually eroded over the past 10–15 years. Society is taking on more and more responsibilities for young people before they reach age 18 through juvenile courts, child labor laws, universal education, and aid to dependent children, for example. But, at times, the programs have been set up poorly, administered poorly, funded poorly, and sometimes create worse problems than the difficulties they were supposed to "cure." The admixture of well-intentioned but poorly organized social "authority" with the politics of self-determination and civil rights has made involuntary hospitalizations of adolescents a contentious issue. The primary arguments oftentimes lose sight of what should be the governing principle: the best interests of the child.

## PSYCHIATRIC PLACEMENT VERSUS JUVENILE HALL

In Chapter 3, we recommended that greater efforts be made to rehabilitate children and adolescents charged with crime. In this chapter we will briefly address the degree to which such treatment is best given in a psychiatric treatment program as opposed to a detention center.

Delinquency is a legal, not psychiatric, term. It connotes a rather severe form of antisocial behavior (one invoking court attention), but does not specify a particular psychiatric diagnosis. Psychiatric diagnoses which are related to delinquency are various, and include the forms of conduct disorder (Jenkins et al., 1985), depression

(Puig-Antich, 1982), and "hyperactivity" (Maletsky, 1974). Other data calling attention to heterogeneity in antisocial populations are epidemiological. Although adult antisocial behavior is practically always preceded by childhood antisocial behavior, most childhood antisocial behavior remits (Meeks, 1980). In terms of conduct disorders, the "long-term prognosis for socialized conduct disorders seems to be relatively favorable" (Robins, 1978), but undersocialized forms have worse prognoses (Jenkins et al., 1985). Because antisocial populations are usually heterogeneous, comparison of treatment efficacy between judicial-correctional systems and medical-psychiatric systems is potentially confounded. This is not to say that comparisons are not possible. One might compare the two approaches by using a uniform population of delinquents. However, as we shall see, as the treatment population is more narrowly defined, the treatment methods and approaches of both systems tend to converge. With the most severely antisocial type of youth (judged delinquent by the court), the two systems may not differ!

Treatments of delinquent youth by correctional and psychiatric systems have been tested and reviewed numerous times. Traditional psychiatric treatments are generally disappointing (Levitt, 1971; Meeks, 1980; Shamsie, 1981), although certain favorable results have been found for conduct disordered children when a concomitant diagnosis was specifically treated, for example treatment of depression with imipramine in selected cases (Puig-Antich, 1982). When the residential treatment of severe conduct disorder (and delinquent) youth has involved the psychiatric perspective, it is done so in complex interaction with court systems. It is therefore difficult to cull out psychiatric versus correctional methods for comparisons. There is some consensus that when institutionalization occurs without medical-rehabilitative programs, the results are harmful (Ross & Nelson, 1979).

A crucial question for the treatment of antisocial youth is whether there are efficacious treatments by any system or method. Milder forms of conduct disorder (probably often predelinquent) *may* be treated by "psychiatric" methods, but they often remit spontaneously and often do not come to court attention. More severe conduct disorder (equated with judicial "delinquency") usually does require institutionalized treatment, but the question still remains: Have any treatments proven to be of help? Many studies and reviews are discouraging, but there are exceptions (see Quay, 1979). One example in which some success is claimed is the Eldora Training School Project in Iowa (Jenkins et al., 1985). There, a variety of modalities were applied in a residential setting with behavioral modification and socialization skills learning strategies as the core theoretical approaches. Some, but not all, delinquent behavior were modified by behavioral techniques. The approach of social learning theory is promising but is a somewhat new conception.

## THE RIGHT TO DIE:
## USE OF EXPERIMENTAL TREATMENTS

There was a time when a diagnosis of leukemia in childhood was tantamount to a sentence of death. In the early 1950s the 5-year survival rate for this illness in children was no more than 5–10%. Today, the long-term survival rate is 50% or higher (Pinkel, 1976). The prognosis for cancer of all forms in children is even better, with long-term survival rates of 79–83% being reported (Li et al., 1978). Even more heartening is the fact that the great majority of children with cancer will need no further therapy and will grow up without residual disability once the original disease is successfully treated.

This dramatic improvement represents the fruit of three decades of medical research. In the continuing search for even better survival rates from childhood cancer, experimental cancer treatments continue to be proposed to youngsters and their families, and despite the risks inherent in such treatments, most children suffering from cancer and their parents agree to go ahead. From a humanitarian viewpoint, one hopes that the children who undergo such treatment are under the care of physicians providing unified, yet comprehensive treatment, doctors who are "tuned in" to the child and his or her family as well as to the disease process and its psychological consequences for the child. But in a practical sense, when it comes to "killers" like cancer, we can expect that children and their families will continue to cooperate with medical research, no matter how the experimental therapies are presented to them.

What happens when a hospital suggests experimental procedures when the likelihood of a cure is relatively small, or when the quality of life will be seriously compromised? When can the parents refuse treatment on behalf of the child, or when can children in their own right refuse treatment? Schowalter et al. (1973) report the case of a 16-year-old girl with a chronic kidney disease, glomerulonephritis, who was treated unsuccessfully with renal transplantation, and who then requested that all medical treatments be stopped to let "nature take its course." The girl's parents concurred with her request to be allowed to die. The hospital staff, aware that the girl's life could be prolonged for a considerable time by frequent dialysis, were initially stunned. Psychiatric examination of the patient indicated no evidence of psychotic thinking, and revealed that she had carefully thought out her decision and had fully grasped its implications. Independently, the staff psychiatrist and the nephrologist concluded that the staff had little choice but to comply with the unfortunate teenager's request, making her dying as comfortable as possible for her and providing the opportunity, through daily counseling, for her to change her mind. After a period of disagreement and intense debate among the hospital staff, with review of the bleak medical alternatives the patient faced, a majority of those caring for her came to agree that they would be able to honor her consistent request. Within a few days of the team's agreement to stop treatment, the young girl died.

In discussing the implications of this case, Schowalter et al. (1973) commented that the following safeguards must be put in place in any such situation: 1) It must first be determined whether or not the child has made his or her decision in a rational and informed manner. 2) The child's cognitive capacity to understand death must be assessed. 3) The amount of suffering and the quality of the patient's life must be taken into account. These authors acknowledge that the issue of a child's right to die remains controversial and that not all physicians would agree that a request of this sort be honored under any circumstances.

What of research into diseases far less dramatic than cancer or nephritis and with far fewer life and death implications? Even if an illness is not known as a "killer," it may remove its sufferers from work or from ordinary intercourse with society (schizophrenia, for instance), or it may make it difficult for its sufferers to develop normal childhood skills (mental retardation, for instance). How does the physician convince the child patient and the family to allow research procedures when the gains cannot be measured in life and death results and the procedure itself may be painful, risky, or prolonged? Honest communication between physician and family is probably the most important guideline. Then, fullest benefits to both the child and to the research project are most likely to occur.

## NONTHERAPEUTIC EXPERIMENTAL PROCEDURES

*A Case Vignette:* Tommy, age 6, is an autistic child. Dr. X, an expert on autism and on EEG research, has invited Tommy's parents to bring him to the laboratory to be a subject in a research project in which his brain stem auditory-evoked responses will be recorded. The recording techniques require that Tommy wear a special cap to which electrodes have been attached and that he listen to "click" sounds over a headset. Since Tommy is known not to be deaf, it is unlikely that the procedure will provide any information that will be directly beneficial to him. On the other hand, important information about abnormalities in the auditory pathways in the brain stem might be obtained from this project, which someday could contribute to understanding abnormal brain mechanisms in autism and in other debilitating language and thought disorders of childhood.

Tommy indicates that he is willing to participate, allows the cap and earphones to be placed upon him, and sits down in the armchair to begin the experiment. Five minutes into the procedure he begins to protest, indicating with shouts and tears that he wants to go home. The experiment is stopped and Tommy leaves. A few days later Tommy's parents bring him back to the laboratory in the evening around bedtime. He again allows the cap and earphones to be placed on his head, after which he is put to bed in the experimental laboratory. When he is deeply asleep the experiment is begun and completed without Tommy's awakening.

Faced with Tommy's dissent, and with the added impossibility of obtaining an adequate brain-wave recording in the initial session, the research investigator in our example interrupted and ended the first session immediately. Since an autistic child may protest at any activity that requires close interaction with others, would the investigator have been wrong to have continued over Tommy's objections? Was it right to carry out the experiment at a later time while the autistic child was asleep? What if Tommy had protested the second application of the cap and headset, but his parents agreed anyway that it should be done? What if Tommy were older?

It may be useful to consider also that Tommy's mental age had been calculated from psychological tests and observation to be between 2 and 3 years. Had his mental age been 8 years, his capacity to understand the nature of the procedure might have made his dissent 5 minutes into the first EEG more meaningful. Perhaps it would have been important enough to stop his participation in the project altogether. As will be seen below, there are a number of opinions on the subject of children's enrollment in scientific research investigations.

There are many serious diseases and mentally handicapping conditions for which our state of knowledge is such that research studies aimed at better understanding the cause and treatment of the conditions in question can offer little immediate benefit to participants in the research. Studies aimed at understanding such diagnostic conditions as mental retardation, early infantile autism or serious language handicaps, or schizophrenia in later childhood may possibly benefit the children of the future, but they will usually fail to aid in any direct way the current subjects of the experiments. In recent times, opinion about the participation of children in research from which they stand little or no chance to benefit has engendered not only passionate arguments, but, as might be expected, extremes of opinion. The Helsinki Declaration states, "Clinical research on a human being cannot be undertaken without his free consent after he has been fully informed; if he is legally incompetent, the consent of the legal guardian should be procured" (Campbell, 1974).

The degree to which the Helsinki Declaration can be applied to research projects with children, and especially to children who are unlikely to benefit, has been argued in various ways. In one interpretation, important in that it has influenced the thinking on the subject in Great Britain and the United States, Sir Harvey Druitt advised the Medical Research Council of England to incorporate the following statement into their 1963 guidelines: "In the strict view of the law, parents and guardians of minors cannot give consent on their behalf to any procedures which are of no particular benefit to them and which may cause them some risk of harm." Even more negative viewpoints have been registered: Theologian Paul Ramsey (1976) argues that doing research on a child, without intending to benefit the child directly, is always evil, no matter how great the potential benefit may be to other children or to society. A California case (*Neilson v. Regents,* 1973) challenges the validity of proxy consent for research on infants.

Others take a more moderate stance: Skegg (1977), who is on the faculty of law at Oxford University, states, "Children who are capable of understanding and coming to a decision on what is involved in non-therapeutic experimental procedures are as able as adults to give a legally effective consent to such procedures. . . . Where a child is incapable of consenting on his own behalf a parent may give a legally effective consent to non-therapeutic procedures which are in the public interest and are not in any significant way detrimental to the child's interests. The procedure need not be for the benefit of the child." He based his opinion on English law and upon a Canadian court decision on the subject.

## DEVELOPMENTAL LEVEL AND INFORMED CONSENT

There is agreement that children may, at some age, refuse to accept hospitalization or life-prolonging treatments or to consent to par-

ticipate in a research project, but at what ages are children capable
of exercising these rights? In keeping with the ideas expressed in
Chapter 2, it would appear to us that prior to age 7 or 8, most
children cannot be expected to understand either the rationale for
or the goals of research, nor are they likely to understand fully the
rationale and goals of treatment, except in a very general sense.
Their parents would have to make all related decisions for them.

Based upon our knowledge of the child's widening understanding of cause and effect during middle childhood, and upon the
child's increasing ability to use concrete operations and formal
logic by age 14, we would expect that by 14, most children would be
ready to participate meaningfully in the consent process in regard
to research. Unfortunately for research, however, it would appear
that children's rational capacities apply to their understanding of
what they know best, such as their immediate environment, rather
than to what may be radically new to them, such as an experiment.

A study by Schwartz (1972) verifies this regrettable hypothesis.
Schwartz's study was designed to clarify the nature of hospitalized
children's awareness of their participation in clinical research, with
the hope of determining at what age children could understand
and, therefore, be involved in the decision-making process. The
young subjects were 36 short-statured children who had partici-
pated in investigations of growth-hormone factors. The studies on
them were conducted almost entirely for research purposes; there
was no guarantee that the results would benefit any individual
child. As a group, the children experienced a total of 50 hospitalizations at the Yale Children's Clinical Research Center. Each child
was prepared for the hospitalization by four pediatric faculty members who were considered particularly sensitive to the needs of
youngsters and their families. As part of the project, some children
were seen for multiple visits beginning as early as 6 months to a
year before hospitalization. At the time of first admission the child
was interviewed to obtain a detailed psychological history. During
each hospitalization, observations were made of the child's behavior and speech content by the nursing staff, and at least two
semistructured psychiatric interviews were conducted during the

course of each child's stay. An attempt was made to delineate the child's understanding of the purpose of the hospitalization, knowledge of the procedures, and expectations of benefit.

None of the 17 children under the age of 11, irrespective of intelligence, socioeconomic status, preparation, or prior hospitalization, showed any awareness that the hospitalization had anything to do with research, nor, with the exception of one child, even that he or she was hospitalized in a research unit.

Of the 19 children over 11 years of age, only six were aware that their hospitalization was related to their participation in a research project. Four of the six viewed their hospitalization as a combination of research and treatment. Only two of these youngsters, a 12-year-old girl and a 17-year-old boy, viewed their hospitalization as strictly a research opportunity with no immediate treatment goal. Interestingly, and unfortunately somewhat ominous for the future of clinical research, these two children both became upset during their hospitalizations and refused to participate any further in the research project. The study thus implied that children of all ages usually do not understand research to be done on themselves, and that if—as an exception—they *do* understand, they very likely will not cooperate.

In addition to the children's lack of cognitive understanding of what, for them, was a relatively new experience, Schwartz's results also suggest that unconscious factors, including the wish to be magically relieved of suffering by a doctor, may have made it difficult for the young experimental subjects to perceive matters as they really were. Such factors are, of course, operative in both children and adults, though they may be more obvious in younger individuals.

## SAFEGUARDS FOR RESEARCH

While informed consent is important and concern about assent and dissent must be consistently maintained for, at the very least, all children at or above age 7, there are many questions that cannot be easily resolved, even given the body of formal rules and regulations that has grown like a hothouse plant over the past 10 years. What is needed is a system that permits originality and flexibility of research while qualifying exactly what constitutes an unacceptable or substantial risk for a given child. In the past, the integrity of the investigator was often considered the best protector for the child. More recently this view has been seriously challenged. Enough well-meaning, kind, and considerate investigators have believed so strongly in the importance of their research questions that they came to overvalue the potential benefits their research would have brought about. Single-minded attention to a project may fuel denials of the inherent risks to the child. No research procedure must be carried out at all costs. As Campbell (1974) points out, medical salesmanship is potent business. People strongly wish to believe in their doctor, that he or she will find a better treatment, or even that he or she will produce a cure. Infectious enthusiasm, charismatic salesmanship, or even gentle persuasion on the part of the research investigator may compromise the objectivity of the parent who must give informed consent on behalf of a young child.

In order to provide relatively disinterested but expert advice regarding human subject protection in research, institutions receiving federal support have, over the past two decades, been mandated to develop institutional review boards (IRBs) to review research protocols and make recommendations aimed at decreasing subject risk. When the risks are considered too great, such review bodies have the power to refuse permission for the project to be carried out. These committees are under the supervision of not only their home institutions but also the federal granting agencies. Since the operation of the boards is linked to funding, the IRBs hold both power and accountability. Whenever they consider projects involving youngsters, IRBs must address such questions as: Are there any better ways to obtain the information at less risk to the subject? Has adequate preliminary research been carried out in animals? Are the possible results worth the risks? Are the consent forms as clear as possible? IRBs must insist that investigators obtain the best possible informed consent from child subjects. Members of IRBs are often in a position of asking themselves whether they would permit their own child to participate in the research project currently under discussion. We believe these questions should be asked.

How well are child subjects currently protected by IRBs? In an evaluation of the IRBs at 61 institutions randomly selected from the more than 420 institutions with review committees approved by NIMH, Gray et al. (1978) reported that review boards had some direct impact on approximately half of the proposals reviewed, either by requiring modification of the research proposal or by asking the researcher to provide more information to the prospective subjects. They noted that consent forms still tend to be incomplete and too difficult for the ordinary person to understand.

## DISCUSSION

We believe that chronological age is not the appropriate measure for determining at what point a child can refuse hospital treatment or demand discharge. Developmental level, which will vary from child to child, is a better determinant. We do conclude, however, that by age 14, most children of normal education and intelligence should have developed a sufficient adeptness with abstract principles to possess the right to demand and receive an outside medical opinion about the necessity of psychiatric treatment before beginning to undergo this treatment involuntarily. Thus, we believe in case-by-case legal handling of children who refuse to consent to treatment, but we also suggest an outside psychiatric opinion for anyone over 14 who requests one.

Insofar as research is concerned, there is little disagreement that above age 14, all potential subjects must give their informed consent separate from their parents. Although the results of Schwartz's study at Yale (1972) show that there are some differences between the thinking of 14-year-olds and of adults, there is no reason to believe that the average 14-year-old is much less capable of making a decision about participation in research than would be the average adult. Below 14 years of age, a child's agreement to participate in a research project is essential, but this assent alone would have no legal force because parents have legal responsibility for such children.

Below 14 years of age, the issues of "assent" and "dissent" are more important and "consent" less important.

The National Commission for Protection of Human Subjects of Biomedical and Behavioral Research (1977) has recommended that all children whose mental age is 7 and older must give their assent before they may participate in research. This seems reasonable enough to our committee, for even if young school-aged children may not understand much about the project in question, this safeguard at least insures that children who are particularly fearful or confused about the research project will not be forced to participate. Below age 7, the question of assent becomes more difficult to decide, and below age 3 assent can hardly be an issue given the limited cognitive and language capacities of the child. Between 4 and 7 years, the child may not understand the concept of research, but may feel fearful nonetheless, especially if the research procedure is a medical one. The best solution may be to address consent, assent, and dissent on a project-by-project basis, using the institutional review board (IRB) of the hospital or medical center as an additional safeguard. If children whose mental age is 7 years or greater must give their assent to research, then it follows that they be allowed the right of dissent.

The National Commission for the Protection of Human Subjects (1977) did, in fact, recommend that research investigators honor the dissent of minors, but no lower age limit was given. If carried to the limit, the Commission's recommendations implied that any baby or toddler who cried during a research activity could automatically call off his or her participation in the research. The Department of Health, Education and Welfare (now Health and Human Services) chose not to implement the recommendation of the National Commission at the time they considered its proposals (1978), but instead proposed that university and hospital institutional review boards decide on a project-by-project basis whether a child's assent would be necessary.

We agree with the principle enunciated by the Health and Human Services Department. We are committed to the continuing expansion of research activities in child psychiatry as long as medical practitioners carry out thorough safeguards for the individual child's well-being. National Institutes of Health and National Institute of Mental Health research review committees are mandated by federal regulations to consider human subject protection and informed consent when they review new research proposals. This is an important safeguard to chidren's rights, properly standing between the researcher and the child subject. We applaud these institutional safeguards and recommend that medical practitioners continue to monitor themselves regarding research on children. Only the science of medicine can understand and evaluate the importance of basic, and often not immediately applicable, studies and the counterbalancing fear and suffering in the child subject who is being asked to undergo such studies.

## REFERENCES

Campbell, A.G.M., (1974). Infants, children and informed consent. *British Medical Journal, 3,* 334–338.

Cooke, R.E., (1977). An ethical and procedural basis for research on children. *Journal of Pediatrics, 90,* 681–682.

Department of Health, Education and Welfare. (1978, July 21). Proposed regulations for research on children. *Federal Register, 48,* 31783–31794.

Gray, B.H., Cooke, R.A., & Tannenbaum, A.S., (1978). Research involving human subjects. *Science, 201,* 1094–1101.

Inglefinger, F., (1972). Informed (but uneducated) consent. *New England Journal of Medicine, 287,* 465–66.

Jenkins, H., Heidemann, P., & Caputo, J. (1985). *No single cause: Juvenile delinquency and the search for effective treatment.* College Park, MD: American Correctional Association.

Levitt, E. (1971). Research in psychotherapy with children. A. Bergin & S. Garfield (Eds.), *Handbook of psychotherapy and behavior change: An empirical analysis* (pp. 474–494).

Li, F.P., Myers, M.H., Heise, H.W., & Jaffe, N. (1978). Course of five-year survivors of cancer in childhood. *Journal of Pediatrics, 93,* 185–187.

Maletsky, B. (1974). D-amphetamine and delinquency: Hyperkinesis persisting? *Diseases of the Nervous System, 35,* 543–547.

Medical Research Council. (1963). *Responsibility in investigation of human subjects.* London: MRC.

Meeks, J. (1980). Conduct disorders. In H.I. Caplan, A.M. Freedman & B.J. Sadock (Eds.), *Comprehensive textbook of psychiatry* (Vol. 3). Baltimore: Williams & Williams.

National Committee for the Protection of Human Subjects of Biomedical and Behavioral Research. (1977). *Report and recommendations: Research involving children.* Washington, DC: DHEW Publication No. OS 77-0004.

Pinkel, D. (1976). Treatment of acute leukemia. *Pediatric Clinics of North America, 23* (1) 117–130.

*Neilson vs. Regents of the University of California,* Plaintiffs Complaint, County of San Francisco, as amended Dec. 20, 1973.

Puig-Antich, J. (1982). Major depression and conduct disorder in prepuberty. *Journal of the American Academy of Child Psychiatry, 21,* 118–128.

Quay, H. (1979). Residential treatment. In H. Quay & J. Werry (Eds.), *Psychopathological Disorders of Childhood* (pp. 387–410). New York: Wiley.

Ramsey, P. (1976). The enforcement of morals: Non-therapeutic research with children. *Hastings Center Report, 6,* 21–30.

Robins, L. (1978). Study of childhood predictors of adult antisocial behavior: Replications from longitudinal studies. *Psychological Medicine, 8,* 611–622.

Ross, A., & Nelson, R. (1979). Behavior therapy. In H. Quay & J. Werry (Eds.), *Psychopathological disorders of childhood* (pp. 303–335). New York: Wiley.

Schwartz, A.H. (1972). Children's concepts of research hospitalization, *New England Journal of Medicine, 287,* 588–592.

Schowalter, J.E. (1978). The minor's role in consent for mental health treatment. *Journal of the American Academy of Child Psychiatry, 17,* 505–513.

Schowalter, J.E., Ferholt, J.B., & Mann, N.M. (1973). The adolescent patient's decision to die. *Pediatrics, 51,* 97–103.

Shamsie, S. (1981). Antisocial adolescents: Our treatments do not work–Where do we go from here? *Canadian Journal of Psychiatry, 26,* 357–364.

Skegg, P.D.G. (1977, October 8). English law relating to experimentation on children. *The Lancet,* p. 754–55.

# 5

## THE MORAL IMPERATIVE: SOCIAL AND PERSONAL "RIGHTS" OF CHILDREN AND ADOLESCENTS

In previous chapters, we have addressed issues relating to the legal rights of children, those "hard rights," as interpreted by the law, that create the dos and don'ts for certain age groups. The topics discussed in this present chapter, however, are not rights at all in the legal sense of the word. Instead, we present the social and personal needs of children, which flow from an ethic, from the wish to enable all children to develop their personality and talents to the fullest capacity. The "soft rights" we discussed in this chapter are subjective and, thus to some extent, matters for discussion and debate. In part, this chapter will focus upon what might best be called "guideposts for parenting." These principles are not generally written into law, but they are de facto outgrowths of society's traditional values and beliefs. As might be expected, they must take into account the child's developing capacities for understanding and for emotional control.

### THE SOCIALIZATION OF CHILDREN: GENERAL PRINCIPLES

The principles that guide society's structures for the socialization of children reflect the children's own expanding social universe. Children's recognition of their primary nurturing "parent" soon expands to encompass the whole family, and later, broadens to include the neighborhood. During latency and adolescence, enlargement of the children's world to include friends, school, and community leads them to make greater demands for independence. By adolescence, autonomy becomes a primary wish. Parallel with this process, children exhibit a greater potential to act with responsibility with each new stage of development. This may in turn be reflected in what parents and society actually allow youngsters to do.

There are two forerunners of social contract theory which suggest, though they do not make explicit, the limits of the developing child's moral claims. The first is the Hobbesian position that the essential nature of humanity is exploitative. According to this principle, contracts are made on the basis of the understanding that human beings are created with equally destructive potentials; only by curtailing these vicious tendencies can mankind live well. The second view is best exemplified by Rousseau: In Savagery and immaturity lies innocence. In this latter view, humanity's natural tendency is to strive toward creative self-determination, especially if the malevolent force of adult civilization does not interfere.

Freud's view of human behavior, curiously, is amenable to inter-pretations of social contracting derived from either Hobbes or Rousseau. Since Freud (1911) viewed children as sentient organ-isms who must give up their immediate selfish needs and "uncivi-lized" wishes in order to join society and live by the reality principle, he saw the human condition as one of inevitable inner conflict. A mastery of this internal conflict through repression would create the social order.

In his psychoanalytically derived view of the "true self," Winnicott (1965) considered privacy and self-determination as highly valued developmental goals for the young person. Self-esteem and a sense of entitlement to various moral expectations would grow from the strength of the adolescent's character. A failure in achieving Winnicott's developmental goal of individuality often occurs in the United States, according to Riesman (1965). "Other-directedness," a supposedly US developmental goal, in which children imbibe others' motives and behaviors, eventually accepting these as part of the self, is something that Riesman sees as a US problem. Riesman asserts that cooperation between individuals is not stressed in the US; rather alertness to the opinions of others takes precedence over self-determination. In Riesman's view, affiliative longings often go unrequited in the US and tribal belonging is hard to achieve.

An example of the sacrifice of personal goals to the collective social aim may occur in some kibbutzim of Israel. A visiting group of US mental health professionals recommended to one group of kibbutz leaders that children living on their collective farm be permitted to own a few objects and toys. But this suggestion ran contrary to the aims of the collective. It was seen as inappropriate in view of the particular kibbutz's aims of mutual cooperation.

Thus, each society's moral entitlements for youth are determined by the particular nature of the society's aims and values. Individuality and conformity are two opposing goals, yet neither can exist entirely without the other.

## EARLY SOCIALIZATION

Let us examine two simple societal demands made upon nursery age children: taking turns and sharing. In early childhood education, these two rules are viewed as one block in the foundation for later reciprocal respect among human beings. Despite a teacher's goals for the preschoolers, however, some children's parents may not reinforce the idea of sharing or taking turns. Some parents condition ambitious, aggressive behavior in their youngsters, whereas others encourage passivity and compliance. Whichever extreme of training a parent may take (and most take a middle ground), the individualistic element in the mental life of young children has to be strongly considered, since there is no question that a private life and individual ambition are developing at the same time that social mores are being incorporated into the personality.

School and family are often primarily concerned with socialization, often at the expense of individuality. The following case vignette illustrates a conflict between the spoken school and parental aims at socialization with the unspoken familial goals of individualism for the child.

> *A Case Vignette:* An upwardly mobile middle-class family sent their 5-year-old boy to a prestigious kindergarten where traditional values of restraint were clearly the rule. The child's behavior, however, was more consonant with his father's aggressive stance at work and in social life than with the school's demands. When the kindergarten teacher complained about

the child's disruptive behavior, the father was genuinely alarmed that his son did not comply, but he continued unconsciously to encourage the child's clear identification with his own aggressive behavior. The boy's sense of dissonance between what was covertly expected by his father and what was overtly demanded by the school made for increasing internal turmoil in the lad.

The developing social needs of children extend both into their public lives and their private worlds. Children's and adult's fantasies are partly composed of those residues of public life that are nurtured privately. These residues are gradually spun into more comfortable thought arrangements, which permit children to compensate for the very real frustrations and losses they encounter. Both the public and private worlds of a child must be considered when we look at children's general social needs. These needs include: 1) the need for privacy; 2) the need for respect; 3) the need to play and to be a child; and 4) the need for autonomy and control.

## THE NEED FOR PRIVACY

Even in the toddler years, the need for privacy is sufficiently important that one might ask if parental intervention is needed when quiet play between peers is going smoothly. The parent must determine how much excitement is to be permitted in preschool and latency games with sexual overtones (as in playing "doctor" or "house," for instance) by estimating each individual child's capacity to understand and to respond to what is meant either by the play itself or by the adult approaches to that play. Parents must continually weigh the consequences of interrupting a youngster's play versus letting it go on. The child's excitement may spiral to the point of discomfort, requiring a parental intervention. On other occasions the youngster's learning opportunities under conditions of play will be invaluable.

Early respect for a child's privacy is important. Parents require privacy, too, especially in the bedroom. A certain natural quid pro quo must develop within the family. Unless children are granted a certain degree of privacy, themselves, they cannot come to understand their parents' needs in this same realm. The separation of the generations, something that has more psychological pros than cons behind it, cannot come about without these privacies, these reminders that certain worlds cannot be entered by those one generation away.

The extent to which privacy is extended often becomes an explosive issue once early adolescence is reached. At this stage bath privacy is assumed, dressing privacy expected, and privacy to talk alone to peers, either by phone or in a separate room, mandatory. Adolescents consider themselves entitled not to be publicly shamed by parents or teachers for their interests, desires, and wishes. Pubertal youngsters' feelings regarding their bodies are often better mastered alone or with agemates rather than by talking with or observing parents. Adolescents may wish to talk with their elders, but their experimental laboratory remains within the realm of peers. They must be allowed the opportunity to pursue relatively harmless "experiments" away from their elders.

Masturbatory activities carry considerable psychological importance during adolescence; the hows and wherefores and specificities of adolescents' self-stimulating endeavors represent a private journey to a place where psychosexual excitement and personal fantasy are tested to their limits. Masturbation is not easily influenced by external coercion. This private travelogue gradually introduces youth to a future destination in which the solitary enjoyment of adolescence will become extended to the mutual enjoyment of adult sexuality. As long as an adolescent's masturbation remains private, parents, school, and religious professionals would be well-advised to glance away, or at the very least, to look upon the issue of masturbation with some leniency. For many children, solitary sexual practice plays an essential part in "growing up."

## THE NEED FOR RESPECT

Children, like adults, wish to be consistently respected. Even an infant will scream with "murderous" intent if crossed. And yet, at times, parents "know" that they are in the right and that their children will suffer seriously if allowed to have their own way.

When considering the issue of parental "coercion," an extreme view might hold that childhood carries with it an entitlement to pleasure, no matter what it is. Another extreme position in this same vein would hold that nothing should be imposed on a child from the outside, especially by a parent. "Nature is the best teacher!" Such wildly hands-off approaches to childrearing do not respect the "soft right" every child holds to parental guidance. Nor do these extremes acknowledge that at each stage of development, respect implies that the child's behavior be governed by new and different parental rules. Preventing toddlers from running out into the street is taken by 2-year-olds as an aggressive restraint, a forced encroachment on their all-important omnipotence. On the other hand, grabbing toddlers out of roadways can be lifesaving. Nobody ever said that good parenting wins child-sponsored popularity contests. On the other hand, the compulsively rule-making and protective parents may inhibit their children's growth.

> *A Case Vignette.* A 16-year-old girl, Laura, was referred for evaluation of a depression that was allegedly based on social ostracization by her peers at a highly competitive academic boarding school. The history given by Laura's parents, both of whom were social workers, revealed a gradual withdrawal from school and social activities 2 months after starting at the new boarding school. Laura's development up to then had been quite satisfactory. The parents had decided to raise their daughter to be free of sexual guilt. Nudity was open, sexual questions and behaviors were condoned, and contraceptive measures had been explained and provided by the parents. Laura said that though she had done well academically, her peers in the new school viewed her as a "slut." They never invited her to parties. She accepted the offer for a course of psychotherapy. Over the period of a year, Laura learned to keep her "openness" private. She became an acceptable, though "reformed," classmate at her school.

*A Second Vignette.* An 8-year-old girl requested that she be able to visit at a friend's home for a weekend. Patricia's mother, however, found out that her child would not be cared for by the girlfriend's mother, but by somebody else whom Mrs. P did not know. Although the child protested loudly when her mother did not grant permission for the overnight, Patricia was later overheard telling a friend that it was just as well that she didn't go. "After all," she said, "a kid wouldn't know if she'd be protected unless the kid's mother could tell how well the other mother was taking care of her own children." This 8-year-old "analysis" might sound like a thinly veiled rationalization, but it also represents an identification with the temporarily unpopular mother and a sense of being highly valued by a parent who, although protective, did not yield to 8-year-old Patricia.

## THE NEED TO PLAY AND TO BE CHILDISH

The need to be immature during childhood was tacitly acknowledged by early 20th century American society when the child labor laws were enacted. These laws, which placed restrictions on the workplace exploitation of children and put prohibitions upon families who had used their youngsters as sources of support, became necessary in our highly specialized industrial society of the 1900s. The children of such heavily specialized societies go to school for relatively long periods and the distinctions between work and play are quite sharp. In preindustrialized communities, on the other hand, children work at home to help their families survive; they help to produce the food, sustenance, and shelter. Play and work are not distinct one from the other. Children, in nonspecialized pre-industrialized communities, more quickly learn the roles and the skills of their parents.

John Dewey wrote of the "naturalism" of the play-work relationship on the old American frontier. At the time of the greatest US expansion, children grew up working, fighting, and caring for younger siblings at their parents' sides. They did not attend schools separate from the home. Frontier youngsters learned to use their natural skills and they took on the solid homespun values of their families. The fruits of their labors were admired and used by the family in everyday life. Youthful migration to the western frontier became incorporated into the American myth. The collective dreams and fantasies of young Americans longing to leave home led to considerable planning and to real choices for some. The story, for instance, of Benjamin Franklin's successful escape from home during his early adolescence and his self-discoveries as a printer's apprentice in Philadelphia is as much a feature of "the American dream" as is the ideal of the colonial rebellion or the legends of unlimited wealth.

In the late 19th century urban hardships made the dependence upon children as supplementary sources of income a way of life for many American families. In the late 19th and early 20th centuries, the highly specialized factories that were growing throughout America found they could operate more effectively if they stayed in operation for longer hours and for longer work-weeks.

American society gradually became aware that young children were being exploited as a labor force. The child's inherent "soft right" to childhood began to be apparent. This realization became codified into the child labor laws, as well as into the concept of universal free education. When compulsory education expanded into the adolescent years, school became modern American society's substitute for the older traditions of work. School also came to offer sanctioned play. Recess, gym, industrial apprenticeship programs, music, and art became essential parts of school curricula as the 20th century came to its midpoint.

By the late 1980s an irony came to "work" or "play" here in the United States. Although our society has granted children longer hours for school, study, and play (rather than for work), youngsters did not consistently take advantage of this time to achieve the more intense specialization that we expected of them. Instead they heeded the ever-present "pied piper," the television set. We at GAP know (see Report 112) that a slavish addiction to the television set carries with it a negative impact on emotional growth. Children cannot meet their own needs for play or self-education by sitting for hours before a mesmerizing box. Aside from television, however, there are further reasons to be concerned that today's children are not playing enough. Growing up too soon and too fast may be a serious contemporary problem.

The "right" to play, or to be a child, includes a child's entitlement to a rich fantasy life. Youngsters require the time and the privacy to work out their internal conflicts and emotional concerns through the medium of "pretend." The complexity of fantasy eventually advances, in accord with maturational sequences, into the playing of more formal, structured games. In the hands of young children, especially unsupervised youngsters forming their own natural groups, games become an important medium within which are played out some of the conflicts and problems of everyday child-life. A significant learning component of such latency and adolescent group games is the mastery of skills which will be important later in working or in living, as adults, with others.

Opie and Opie's *The Lore and Language of School Children* (1959) is an interesting testimony to how the games of middle childhood are transmitted orally through the generations throughout the English speaking world with barely a change in wording. Jumprope rhymes, hopscotch rhymes and preschool circle games have hardly changed at all. This oral transmission suggests something universal about the play of childhood. A retrospective look into the past emphasizes these continuities. Bruegel's painting, "Children's Games," for instance, shows us that most games played during the 17th century remain quite familiar. Twenty-first century youngsters will probably continue to act like their predecessors, despite the technologically sophisticated electronic games and computer graphics that are catching on so fast in late twentieth century America. The conflicts and developmental tasks of childhood remain relatively fixed, although there certainly will be variations for each age of civilization.

Children need to play in order to master their future expectations, to deal with their internal conflicts, to cope with peer groups and with rules, and to handle externally generated frights and life stresses. Adequate opportunity to play sharpens children's ability to recognize their needs and to deal with them effectively, preparing them for the work that is to come.

## THE NEED TO GAIN AUTONOMY AND
## TO ACHIEVE PERSONAL CONTROL

Although toilet training may be considered a form of early social control, it is also a paradigm for a childhood trade-off: youngsters give their compliance and get in return love and approval from their parents. Although many parents no longer toilet train before a child's neurodevelopmental capacities for bowel and bladder control are developed, many others still precipitously toilet train because a new baby has arrived, grandma demands it, or the local nursery school or daycare center refuses children in diapers.

Some mothers and fathers, at the opposite extreme, look to toilet training as a kind of negotiation in which children, themselves, should participate, not only in the process, but in the decision to start the process. This notion runs contrary to what we know about the stormy, self-centered emotional makeup of normal children under 3 years. While some cultures toilet train by using shame (some Native American cultures, for instance), this shaming takes place at a later time in the child's life than does Caucasian American toilet training. Thus, when Caucasian American mothers suggest that their children go to the potty on their own accord, they are overlooking an important developmental fact, that children will go to the potty themselves only if the parents are clear that they want him to do so, and usually only if they show some insistence to back their encouragement.

By contrast, consider the parents' role when they send their children to school. The children are no longer "all alone," as they were during the time of toilet training. Society does not expect that parents will in any way negotiate the children's obligation to attend school; this developmental plan, as opposed to toilet training, is so inbred in our culture that it seems entirely natural and unforced to expect youngsters to comply. Society expects that 5- or 6-year-old children will anticipate that they *are* going to school, and that they will be expected to conform there. The skill requirements of school may seem vague to children, but the social requirement that they attend seems natural to ordinary 5- or 6-year-olds.

In thinking about autonomy in the middle years, children's participation in religious activities becomes an important issue. Among parents who are highly committed to their churches, there usually is no question that latency-age children will participate along with them. In families with less conviction, there may be less pressure on children to participate, thus more choice for the children. It is a curious fact, however, that even in relatively irreligious homes, latency-age children may often become deeply interested in religious matters and, thus, tend to exhibit greater piety than their parents. This surge of ethical and religious interest at the same time that the superego takes definite form may account for latency-aged children's need to unmask what they feel to be parental hypocrisies. What better way is there for children to exercise their newfound logic than by demonstrating righteousness and moral superiority? In most matters of religious choice prior to midadolescence, parents remain, however, the legally sanctioned deciders.

Taking parent and latency-aged child clashes into less controversial areas, let us consider the parents who simply want their 8-year-old to take music lessons. The piano teacher tells the parents that the child's success will depend upon a family interest in good music. A question now becomes evident: "Does the family want the youngster to be a virtuoso, musically competent, or simply an appreciative music consumer"? The child should have some choice in this matter.

We believe that entering young children into a field for which they will be required to train themselves to competence requires serious parent-child negotiation. There are realistic questions of talent, interest, and locus of control around the practice and training that will be required of an ambitious youngster. Lessons provide a means to measure children's progression from "learning for love" to "learning for the love of learning." A gifted teacher can accomplish near miracles in "turning children on" to art, to music, to sports, or even to the cultural values of their families. The negotiation process regarding latency-aged children's explorations of art and sport, therefore, depends upon full parental assessment of all relevant data and the children's judgment, too, about what they would like to achieve and how hard they want to work for it.

As children approach adolescence, negotiations between child and parent become more intense. There are few adolescents who do not at some time press for a new and more liberal curfew, more money, full use of the family car, permission for a dangerous exploit, or assent to entertain those of the opposite sex in the bedroom. Parental permission must come after realistic consideration of the dangers and the specific maturities of the particular adolescent. The petitioning teenager holds an entitlement to know what factors lie behind particular parental decisions. Without access to the "reasons," teenagers will almost automatically make pointed judgments about parents' emotional makeup, or parents' trouble accepting their own advancing age.

Let us take a fairly typical parental response, "When you go off to college, you will be able to stay out as late as you like," and look at it from the adolescent's point of view. The teenager, now, hopefully capable of formal thought, logically reasons: "Why is it that, when I am away from home, my actions will be okay, whereas when I am at home, my behavior is not okay?" The parental implication "what I don't know won't hurt me" seems to contradict the very apparent present parental concern. To the adolescent, the parents are somehow saving themselves the trouble of negotiating by taking solace in the idea that a rite of passage, college, will take care of everything. The move out of the home will somehow give permit for difficult decision-making to the young person. Child psychiatrists see, however, that the stage of formal operations gives the teenagers enough reasoning capacities to fully discuss with parents decisions that are made on their behalf while they are still home. Adolescents may protest disagreeably and perhaps rebelliously, but they will learn from negotiating with their parents how to use reasoning skills to cope with difficult interpersonal situations that come up in the future.

It may not hurt adolescents at all to learn that they can occasionally win a well-made argument with their parents. Parental demonstration of growing respect will give new confidence to adolescents as they negotiate those decisions that will be relevant to their lives. Learning the negotiation process accords a sense of responsibility to adolescents that will be useful as they regulate their demands later in life. Negotiation makes adolescents aware that decision making does not have to be a unilateral authoritarian activity based upon personal need, but rather can be a cooperative effort based upon mutual advantage. The later benefits to such negotiations as dealing with a spouse, a boss, the bridge club members, or the body politic will be great, indeed, for adolescents.

## SCHOOLS

If there is one moral imperative that America has granted its children in the last 50 years, it is the right to free and universal schooling. Long sanctified in public opinion and emphasized by the requirement that students remain in school until a certain age, the public belief in the right to education has been given legal status as well as a moral imperative (*Goss v. Lopez*, 1975). In the Goss decision, the court held that "entitlement to a public education is a property interest which is protected by the Due Process Clause." Although intended in the earlier part of this century to apply to primary and secondary schooling, the "right" to a public education has been extended now, through a system of subsidized junior colleges and state universities, well into the adult years.

School has not always been available to young children; at one time in Western history, public education was only provided for young adults and adolescents. In an earlier era, schools were designed for ecclesiastical and secular persons-of-rank to learn Latin and Greek—and to become gentlemen. American schools, however, went through a massive change during the 19th century. Whereas they previously had provided advanced education and training for elite groups, 19th century American schools found themselves melding immigrants from Europe into the American melting pot. In more recent years, the schools have been mandated to supply an education at public expense for every young child and adolescent residing in the United States.

Effective universal education requires students and their families to participate fully in the process and the work of learning. The commitment to participate, unfortunately, is not always made. Schools are no longer, strictly speaking, parts of their neighborhoods, and thus, some families do not take part in their programs. Furthermore, if their schoolwork is to be meaningful for them, students must have the hope of finding reasonable jobs in the future. Discouragement about employment prospects may seriously interfere with students' outlook on their education.

## SCHOOLS AND PERSONAL PRIVILEGES

Within the past few decades, some critics have voiced concern about the moral claims of students. Both law and tradition have upheld teachers' rights to discipline and to exert behavioral control over young persons. The school acts as a substitute parent, and within the school setting, the teacher and principal stand in the parents' stead. School authorities have enjoyed long-standing "rights" to administer corporal punishment to students, to invade the privacy of the students' persons, desks, and lockers, and to enforce prescribed conduct. The balance of power between school and student is a delicate one. To one observer, our schools may be more "hung up on control and discipline" than on education, but to the next, "our teachers are endangered by the increasing violence in our public schools." These issues are complex and difficult to resolve. Everyone in America has a right to an education. Behavioral modulation must be exacted in return.

In addition to the right to a free public education, Levine and Carey (1977) have listed a number of moral entitlements of students. These include:

1) *The "right to free expression of opinion" at any age.* According to interpretations of the First Amendment to the US Constitution, schoolchildren have the right to decline saluting the flag or saying the Pledge of Allegiance. They may wear armbands to protest wars that they oppose, and they may engage in other

unconventional verbal and symbolic behavior. However, free speech and personal expression are granted to students only to the extent that expression of this right does not interfere with the academic programs of the school.

2) *Free choice of dress and personal appearance.* Since one's appearance or choice of costume is a personal affair, dress codes and other codes of personal appearance have a checkered history in US schools. Hair length prescriptions have increasingly been overruled in the courts because they are often used in gender discrimination. Still, this matter is usually left to local courts.

3) *The rights to adequate notice, counsel, and appeal in cases in which suspension or expulsion may come about.* "Considerations of due process" (Fourteenth Amendment) are being invoked more and more to protect chidren who are suspended or expelled from school. Children running the risk of expulsion or temporary removal from school have a recognized right to adequate notice of the charges against them, the right to counsel if the suspension is for more than 10 days, the right to appeal the suspension or expulsion. The Fifth Amendment protects a student's right to remain silent during any disciplinary school hearing.

4) *Rights to silence and privacy in matters of criminal investigation.* Since the schools in the US lack immunity from police intervention, a slim body of rights has emerged regarding search and seizure, police interrogation and investigation. The child does have a right to remain silent when police come to school to ask questions, but the child holds no right to the privacy of his/her person against search without a warrant of his/her body, desk or locker. There is a current trend to give some protection to students against "unwarranted" drug screens of their blood or urine, against physical examinations, and against questionnaires that probe into "intimate matters" such as their sexuality or the intimate lives of their parents.

5) *Freedom from corporal punishment.* There has been no protection against beating, caning, or spanking of schoolchildren since the Supreme Court decision *Ingrahm v. Wright* (1976). At this point in the United States, only members of one age group, children,

can be beaten. A countervailing trend to enact laws against child abuse has arisen, however, in recent years.

6) *Freedom from racial, religious, ethnic, and gender discrimination.* Protection against discrimination has been guaranteed by numerous judicial rulings and US laws, but some schools persist in practicing racial segregation. In areas that generally accept neighborhood segregation, school segregation is supported and defended as "only natural when people attend a school near their home." Increasing rights are being guaranteed against sex or gender discrimination. Most of these have been applied to school athletics and extracurricular offerings.

7) *Freedom from discrimination based upon being a parent, being pregnant, or being married.* This type of discrimination against young women in the schools has been slow to die. Not only do the statutes of most states allow a young mother to continue in school if she desires, but in most states motherhood is a basis for application to leave school, should that be desired.

8) *Right to access to school files.* New entitlements and protections have been accorded to students regarding their records. The Buckley Amendment of 1974 entitled all students over 18 years of age and the parents of younger students to obtain access to the entirety of their school records (*School Law Bulletin,* 1981). In practice, many barriers have been set up, however, when students seek to read their records or to expunge them. Students (or parents if the youths are under 18) have the right to a hearing if they seek to modify or expunge objectionable material in a cummulative record. Outsiders are forbidden access to school records without parental permission. The privacy and confidentiality of school records are generally respected. However, the contents thereof are, in practice, difficult to modify or to erase.

## ADOLESCENT SEXUAL BEHAVIOR

The fact of sexual activity in the teenage years is now well established. The major problem that the sexual revolution has produced is teenage pregnancy outside of marriage (now over one million cases per year). A study (Jones, 1980) of the children of teenaged parents reports that in comparison to children of older parents of similar economic background, children of teenage mothers show significant decrements in academic achievement, are more likely to live in one-parent or stepparent homes, and tend to repeat youthful parenthoods, themselves. The younger the adolescent mother, the more adverse will be the impact of the pregnancy on both herself and the child. Yet it is this very group of younger teenagers for whom the incidence of childbearing and childkeeping is increasing at a proportionally greater rate than it is for the middle and later stages of adolescence.

Public controversy rages around the issues raised by these youthful pregnancies: abortion, childkeeping, and adoption. Ultimately, however, these public debates must turn back to questions regarding premarital sexual activity and the privileges of youth to obtain contraception. Some would "prohibit" sexual activity until a youngster is "competent." Others suggest that sexual experimentation itself is part of the process of achieving this "competence," or maturation. The first group states that contraception encourages early sexual activity and therefore should be prohibited; the second group believes that contraception should be available to any youngster who is sexually active or who plans to become so. A third alternative proposes that young women under 18 who visit family planning clinics should be served, but their parents should also be informed. All agree that pregnancy is best avoided until, at least, late adolescence. But how to achieve this?

## PREGNANCY AS A DILEMMA: MARRIAGE, ABORTION, KEEPING OR GIVING UP FOR ADOPTION

An American Psychiatric Association Task Force on teenage parents and their children (Fineman, 1979) points out that young teenagers, who are only beginning to learn to master their newly adult bodies and to crystalize their core identities, will find the physiological and psychological demands of pregnancy literally shattering of body and mind. Pregnancy may arrest an adolescent emotionally, physiologically, and cognitively. When a teenager has not yet evolved into a mature person or separated from her parents, she is in no position to think of herself as a mother. The risks of child abuse and neglect, as well as of prematurity, are highest among these young mothers (Bolton et al., 1980; Jones, 1980; Kinard & Klerman, 1980). In the late adolescent, providing that development has proceeded well, pregnancy may also produce regression, though it is more likely to provide a positive maturational opportunity to separate from early attachments.

Schaffer and Pine (1972) studied a series of pregnant adolescent girls who were seeking therapeutic abortions. They found that the pregnancy seemed to bring to the fore a conflict between being mothered and being a mother. There was an arousal and intensification of early passive longings for one's own mother (longings that normally occur during adolescence), mingled with cravings to become a mother to one's infant, to one's self, and to others. New identifications and an attempt to begin life anew characterized at least part of these young pregnant teenagers' psychologies. Although there was conflict in all the girls, Schaffer and Pine found no uniformity in how their ambivalence was handled. A relative balance between cravings to mother and to be mothered (regardless of the stage of adolescence) was the best predictor of how the particular girl would cope with her abortion.

Those needy of mothering themselves coped least well with their abortions, since their personal identification lay with the infant. They allowed their own mothers to make all their decisions and arrangements and to care for them through the entire experience, as if wishing to recapture vicariously their own infancy. Afterwards, this "needy" group tended to continue their sexual activity without contraception, unless birth control pills were practically hand fed to them by their mothers.

At the other extreme, a second group of girls handled the conflict about abortion quite independently. Their coping became the basis for considerable emotional growth. This group found that for the first time they could care for themselves in a major way, and their planning for their abortion became an experience in self-care. Often they did not involve their mothers at all, or if they did, it was in a more advisory and less active way. These girls emerged from the experience with an important sense of mastery, both of their own bodies and of the external world. For this group of girls, the pregnancy and abortion seemed to act as an organizing experience, and an impetus for further development.

Finally, a third group of Schaffer and Pine's teenage abortion subjects initially denied the reality of their pregnancies and, once they acknowledged the facts, delayed making any decisions for varying lengths of time. These girls enlisted the involvement of their mothers, but they attempted to seek outside support, as well. They tried to take an active role in making decisions and arrangements, but this usually occurred within the context of their own mother-child relationship. The investigators considered this a midway position in mastering the developmental task of shifting from a relatively passive "being mothered" position to a relatively more active "mothering" position.

In general, conflicts of pregnancy and abortion are age-related and can be predictably equated with early, middle, and late adolescent stages of development. In general, pregnant 13- and 14-year-olds cannot handle the variety of options offered them. Too frightened to act for themselves, they need decisions to be made for them. The entire immediate family usually has to become involved. Adolescents 15 and 16 years old may require more time to make their decisions, but they often consider various options early in their pregnancies and, as opposed to the younger group, are able to reach their choices with less overt direction from others. Teenagers 17 and 18 years old are usually mature enough to consider their options, and when provided with adequate information and support, they seem to be able to reach decisions independently.

Stages of development and conflicts concerning mothering and being mothered impinge upon a teenager's ability to make reasonable decisions regarding pregnancy. Life circumstances differ. If little of interest is happening in the teenager's life, if she can't stand things at home, if her school performance is poor, if her social experience is not satisfying, and if the prospect of a baby fulfills the need to be loved by someone else, then the teenager may wish to continue the pregnancy and keep the child, for clearly the "wrong" reasons. Such an event reminds us once again of the limitations of "legal rights" that are set up strictly according to the child's age.

*A Clinical Vignette.* Sally, age 14, was seen at the family planning clinic for an early pregnancy test. Sally had temporarily dropped out of school and her only ongoing social contact was her boyfriend. The young teenager showed a very low self-regard. In the sexual act, Sally felt little genital gratification. She wanted to be held and cuddled and to please her boyfriend in the hopes that she might hold his attention. She used no contraception, which at first glance seemed to reflect the lack of control of her own life. (Her boyfriend had told her contraceptives were dangerous and could cause cancer, and she had believed him.) When presented with abortion as an important option, Sally told her social worker that she was against the "murder of another human being." She wanted to keep her baby.

Sally's parents were interviewed separately, and they indicated that they would no longer support her if she carried the pregnancy to term, even though they loved her very much; they felt she was not at all ready to be a mother. The family was then brought together for an interview because the pregnancy seemed to be a problem affecting them all. Options of abortion or adoption were presented by the social worker as alternatives to keeping the new baby in the family. Sally refused adoption, saying that it would be too painful to go through the loss of her own flesh and blood. The decision for abortion seemed to be forced upon her since all other options were being eliminated. But Sally still could not decide for herself.

The clinic worker gave Sally a raw egg. They drew a cute baby face on it with a magic marker and pasted on some fuzz for hair. Sally was to pretend it was a baby, a very delicate thing that she had to care for 24 hours a day without breaking. The 14-year-old took her egg to school, but she felt constantly worried about it. She could not study. She awakened several times at night to look on her chest of drawers to see if the egg had rolled off and broken. She let her boyfriend keep the egg for a day; he gave it back early because it kept him from doing anything with the guys and from going "all out" during baseball practice. Both children came back to the clinic in three days and said that they had decided upon abortion as their way to deal with eggs! Sally had her abortion and did quite well emotionally after it.

## CONTRACEPTION

Traditionally, the ages of 14–17 have been considered the age of "practicing," and some form of sexual experimentation with peers of the opposite sex is part of that practicing period. Experimentation with intimacy may include full sexual activity for some adolescents. While providing contraceptive advice and materials is equated by some people with sanctioning premature sexual activity, contraception may provide an important part of learning and decision making for the sexually active youngster, irrespective of age. Realistically, it is unlikely that a significant number of teenagers would cease their sexual activities if they had to obtain their parents' consent before obtaining any contraceptive aids or information. Indeed, making contraceptives difficult to obtain without parental approval might produce conflict, distance, and less positive interactions within the families of adolescents. More meaningful relationships with the opposite sex will occur by ages 18 or 19 years. At the end of the teens, mature decisions about sexual behavior can be made.

The AIDS epidemic currently most rampant among homosexuals, intravenous drug users, hemophiliacs, and those who indulge in sex with people whom they do not know well has already impinged on the adolescent "world." The spread of AIDS functions as a cautionary tale. There is good reason to believe that teenagers may become far more conservative about the type of "sexual practice" they choose and the kind of partner they pick for that "practice" than they are today.

## SEX EDUCATION

> *A Case Vignette.* A psychiatrist was called early one Sunday
> morning by a neighbor who was in a state of anxiety and
> wanted to talk immediately about the fact that he had just
> traumatized his two young sons, aged 5 and 11. He related that
> on the previous evening he and his wife had entertained
> guests and offered much wine and had shown "blue stag"
> movies to all. In their haste to retire they left the film projector
> and screen in place. The boys awoke early and looked at the
> films. When asked about it, the 11-year-old was quite
> embarrassed, anxious, and remarked, "Is that what it is?" The
> 5-year-old asked, "What is going on? What is happening?"—
> with some vague reference to the bathroom. The issue was
> dropped. When the father asked them about it 10 years later,
> the then 11-year-old had a vague memory of it and the
> 5-year-old had no conscious recollection.

Surveys have shown that a high percentage of all Americans
favor sex education in the schools. Opponents feel that sex education belongs solely in the home or at church. Today, only about
10% of our high school students are exposed to a comprehensive
sex education program. The rest receive substantially less or nothing at all.

Introduced by school systems in the late 1960s, many sex education programs became "too controversial" and then withered away.
Many were poorly organized. Parents were concerned that too
much "information" about sexual activity (including illustrations
and information about contraception and abortion) would encourage precocious sexual experimentation. The mass effort to provide
sex education in the schools has largely failed.

## DISCUSSION

We believe that, hard as it may be, a delicate balance must be
achieved between chidren's ever-changing needs to be protected
and the same children's needs to learn through "hard knocks." This

balance can be especially difficult to attain at the two most willful stages of childhood: the toddler years and adolescence.

The "soft rights" of children grow more extensive and more complicated throughout the developmental cycle. These moral rights must be adjusted and reconsidered at each stage of development for each individual child. They must relate to the child's special needs as well as to his or her unique capacities to control him/herself and to cope with his or her environment.

"Soft rights" materialize in a context that includes an integration between the home and the larger community. Parents must take positions consonant with public values, yet they must also seek positions in accord with private, personal principles. If a well-developed conscience is to become an active force in children's lives, children must gradually learn from their parents how to negotiate, to give-in if wrong, and to stand firm if convinced that they are right. A balance between individuality and conformity must be struck in any child's eventual personality structure. In the course of childrearing, however, one or the other of these may temporarily take precedence.

Nowhere else in this book are the actual chronological ages less meaningful, the developmental stages more important, and a flexible, individualized approach to every child more crucial than in regard to the ethical and moral rights of young people. Childrearing tasks are seldom legislated or heard in courtrooms; instead, they develop within the home. It is rightly left to parents to set children's religion, require them to attend church, take them to the doctor, establish their diet, cut their hair, dress them, punish them, and within reason use their property and money. Children can be sent protesting to camp, to babysitters, or to the outdoors or the indoors by their parents. Many years ago children were considered by courts to be their parents' property. Some of this proprietary attitude still remains alive in our modern day households and at our schools.

We suggest that a child will not fully develop if handled like parental property. From the time youngsters begin to drop food from the highchair onto the floor, they are developing minds of their own and pride in their unique individuality. Parents who do not attend to this self-growth or who suppress it may cripple their children emotionally, though no court will intervene on the children's behalf. At the opposite side of the spectrum, parents may give in automatically to their children's demands, crippling them through bounty rather than through deprivation. Both of these approaches, absolutist and laissez faire, may be crippling to youngsters, depending, of course, upon their own nature, flexibility, and reasoning skills. But courts or legislatures will have nothing to do with these aspects of childrearing.

If, as psychiatrists, we could say just one word to parents about childrearing, it would be "communicate." Communication must be equi-flowing from parent to child and from child to parent. The communication should be filled with emotional expression, understanding, intellectual effort, and humor. It will improve, of course, as the years pass. But it must first exist before it can improve. Good, meaningful communication with parents is the most important "soft right" of childhood. With it, children will proceed best past the humps of privacy issues and the concerns about respect, sexuality, school, religion, and moral values.

In regard to sexual behavior, we believe it is now time to rethink sex education and to reconstruct voluntary and comprehensive pilot programs in our schools. Schools must take the responsibility for helping develop formal operational thinking in their students, instead of assuming that youngsters come to school equipped with it. Schools may assume that adolescents will consider options and find solutions if they are provided with enough "information," but sex is not simply a matter of the "facts," it involves sophisticated decision-making skills.

We also believe that the American school-aged child is entitled to a family-life education. Teaching "the facts of life" is only one part of this task. Well-planned pilot programs in the schools, with parental participation in the planning, would provide the opportunity for students to explore the relationships between the sexes, to consider what constitutes ethical and moral behavior, and to respect the passionately differing opinions regarding these very basic issues. Children receiving continuing, developmentally appropriate education in family life would be able to role-play or to practice how to make crucial decisions after considering all the options.

Considering all the options has the tendency to raise more questions than it gives answers. Each young person must search for ways to make intelligent, ethical decisions for him- or herself. Classes in family life might improve communication between parents and their teenage children. Good intrafamilial communication, in and of itself, may reduce compulsive and self-defeating teenage sexual activity.

Ninety percent of a good sex education should revolve around the development of human relations, the formation of values, and the building of decision-making skills.

## REFERENCES

Bolton, F.G., Jr., Laner, R.H., & Kane, S.P. (1980). Child maltreatment risk among adolescent mothers: A study of reported cases. *American Journal of Orthopsychiatry, 50*, 480–504.

Fineman, J. (1979, September 21). *APA Task Force on Teenage Parents and Their Children, position paper.* Washington, DC: A

Freud, S. (1911). Formulations on the two principles of mental functioning. *Standard Edition, 12*, 213–226. London: Hogarth.

Goss v. Lopez, 419 U.S. 565, 1975.

Ingrahm v. Wright, 430 U.S. 651, 1976.

Jones, S.P. (1980). Teenage pregnancy and motherhood. *American Journal of Orthopsychiatry, 50*, 403–431.

Kinard, E.M., & Klerman, L.V. (1980). Teenage parenting and child abuse: Are they related? *American Journal of Orthopsychiatry, 50*, 481–488.

Levine, A.H., & Carey, E. (1977). *The rights of students: The basic ACLU guide to a student's rights.* New York: Avon.

Opie, I., & Opie, P. (1959). *The lore and language of school children.* London: Oxford University Press.

Riesman, D. (1965). *The Lonely Crowd: A study of the American character.* New Haven: Yale University Press.

Schaffer, C., & Pine, F. (1972). Pregnancy, abortion and the developmental tasks of adolescents. *Journal of the American Academy of Child Psychiatry, 11*, 3.

*School Law Bulletin.* (1981, January). p. 1.

Winnicott, D. (1965). *Maturational process and the faciliatory environment* London: Hogarth.

# 6

## A SPECIAL INSTANCE OF LEGAL RESPONSIBILITY: THE CHILD AS A WITNESS IN COURT

The law and child psychiatry differ significantly in their approaches to the age or the developmental stage at which a child can be allowed to testify, and the age at which the child would be considered believable in court.

These issues are becoming more and more important to child psychiatry now that the question has been raised about using young child witnesses in such cases as the McMartin Preschool sex abuse trial in Los Angeles, or the child abuse-child murder charges that were made in a small town in Minnesota in 1984 and then dropped within a few weeks (*L.A. Daily Journal*, 1987). The legal term "competent to witness" is defined in *Black's Law Dictionary* (1968) as "one who is legally qualified to be heard to testify in a cause." A credible witness is "one who is competent to give evidence; also one who is worthy of belief." Neither the law nor child psychiatry considers a child's competency or credibility strictly by age, but the law does include some age requirements for competency. For instance, in *Wheeler v. U.S.* (1897), the US Supreme Court observed, "No one would think of calling as a witness an infant only two or three years old." There is no fixed statutory minimum age for testifying, however. Several states presume that above a certain age (10, if the state has such a statute, and 14, if the state follows common law) the child is competent to be a witness. These legal presumptions are not binding on the courts, however, if one of the parties or the judge raises the issue of the child's competency (Taub-Katz & Katz, 1980).

Once the question of competency is raised, a "voir dire" examination of the child takes place in court. "This phrase denotes the

preliminary examination which the court may make of one presented
as a witness or juror, where his competency, interest, etc., is objected
to (Black, 1968). Case law and some statutes provide the guidelines
for judicial examination of children who are offered as witnesses.

The law is concerned with the child's intelligence and ability to
truly relate the facts. The law also expects that a competent child
witness would have received an accurate impression of the event at
the time it occurred. Furthermore, courts require that the child
witness has a sense of obligation to tell the truth (*American Jurisprudence*, 1976). Some courts state the youngster must believe in
God or in heavenly punishment in order to take the oath as a
witness (*State v. Belton*, 1885).

A judge is primarily interested in the child's intelligence and
true impressions of the facts at the time of trial. There have been
some cases in which children were disqualified as witnesses because
they had been too young to have an accurate recollection of the
event in question (*Hollaris v. Jankowski*, 1942; *Rosche v. McCoy*, 1959),
but in general, the age and "intelligence" at the time of testimony,
not at the time of the event, are the crucial issue for the law (*Knab v.
Alden's Irving Park*, 1964). To sum up the law's attitude, the following quote from *Wheeler v. US* (1897) is offered: "there is no precise
age which determines the question of competency. This depends
on the capacity and intelligence of the child, his appreciation of
the difference between truth and falsehood, as well as of his duty to
tell the former. The decision of this question rests primarily with
the trial judge, who sees the proposed witness, notices his manner,
his apparent possession or lack of intelligence, and may resort to
any examination which will tend to disclose his capacity and intelligence as well as his understanding of the obligations of an oath."

The law considers that the child's appearance, fear or composure,
general demeanor, manner of answering, and indications of prior
coaching in regard to the testimony to be given are all as significant
as are the words used in answering during the examination (*American Jurisprudence*, 1976). It requires that the child appear personally
before the court for the voir dire examination (*Whitehead v. Stith*,
1937). Until 1982 pretrial hypnosis to "enhance" the child witness's

recall had not been considered to be a form of "coaching or instruction" that would disqualify the child as a witness (Diamond, 1980). However, in the future, cases like the California *People v. Shirley* (1982) may serve to disqualify hypnotized witnesses.

To the child psychiatrist, the 1897 *Wheeler v. US* guidelines for competency of child witnesses appear simplistic and outmoded, an inadequate system which fails to take into account such important subjective factors as motivation, perceptual capacities, suggestibility, and memory. The Supreme Court's guidelines fail to address the issues of child witnessing from a developmental viewpoint, nor do they take into account the stress under which the child may have been, and may still be, operating.

## PERCEPTION AND MEMORY UNDER EXTREME STRESS

Terr's (1981a, 1983a) studies of the kidnapped schoolchildren of Chowchilla indicate that under extreme stress, a significant minority of children visually misperceive or hallucinate (9 of 23 victims within the first year). More commonly, children's sense of time during a traumatic event is distorted (2 of 25 at Chowchilla mixed up night and day, 2 of 25 were disoriented in time, 14 children missequenced the events, and 4 experienced the entire duration as shortened). Children tend to include details from before their traumatic event, and less often from after the event, when considering the entirety of the event. Despite these misperceptions and memories of misperceptions, children may also recall the details of a stressful experience in remarkable detail, relating blow-by-blow accounts of what occurred.

Terr (1983b) conducted a comparative study of 20 children and 10 adults who were separately and individually traumatized and found distorted time sense in a significant number of victims of any age. Some adults and older children who had been exposed to a momentary fright tended to prolong the time over which they believed the event to have occurred. Several individually traumatized victims were entirely confused about the passage of time. Both adults and children formed "omens," appending to their experiences a warning through retrospection.

The visual and timing mistakes that traumatized adults and children experience under conditions of terror lead them to function less well as courtroom witnesses than they would have functioned, if spared from fright. On the other hand, school-age children-witnesses have an advantage over their adult counterparts in one important respect. Children can remember details of their traumatic occurrences (Terr, 1981a) on occasions when adults may remember far less (Horowitz, 1976). In one instance a 12-year-old child and her mother each recalled memories that were quite different of a dog attack upon the youngster. The mother had completely forgotten, indeed was amnesic, about how she had stopped the dog, whereas the girl, 7-years-old at the time she was attacked, remembered in full detail everything that had happened to her. Despite the fact that the dog had slashed open her throat, the child was the better witness. Bystanders confirmed what the child told the court (Terr, 1980).


## HYPNOSIS OF CHILDREN IN LEGAL MATTERS

Hypnosis has been widely used by law enforcement personnel in the attempt to enhance recall by eyewitnesses. Children have been questioned in such sessions. The use of investigative hypnosis in children is highly questionable. Consider, for instance, Andrea, age 14, who was accused of mass murder by her best friend Arlene, also 14. Arlene's accusation came 4 months after the crime was committed, and it was based upon "dreams" of which Arlene had recently become aware. Almost all the evidence against Andrea was contained in a "vision" of the murder which police hypnotists obtained from Arlene. Arlene testified convincingly in court after her hypnotic sessions. Three people she accused were convicted; Andrea, who insisted upon her innocence, was convicted of being an accessory to the murders. There was nothing in Andrea's history, school record, interviews, or behavior in the detention home that coincided with her conviction as a mass-murderer. But a child psychiatrist is not in the position to prove innocence.

Bernard Diamond (1980) tells of a 9-year-old, M, who was hypnotized for "memory enhancement" in a sexual molestation case against her 59-year-old neighbor. In April 1977, the child, with her mother's permission, cleaned the neighbor's house. Several months later, the daughter of the people from whom M's family rented their house came to stay with M's family and told M's mother that the neighbor had molested her child 12 years earlier. M's mother concluded that this must have happened to M the previous April when she cleaned the house. The mother vigorously and repeatedly questioned M, who denied it. In August 1977, M was brought to the local police department, and the child denied that any sexual contact had occurred. She was then taken to a psychologist who specialized in the use of hypnosis for criminal investigation. During the first hypnotic session (there was no psychological history taken or clinical examination done), the child continued her denials. In November 1977, the police officer and the psychologist were present during the second hypnotic session in which the child became upset when told to sit on the policeman's lap. Finally, in a questioning session December 7, 1977, the child dictated to the police a detailed story of a sexual molestation. Dr. Diamond testified that "the child's subsequent testimony was so contaminated by the hypnotic experience that no cross-examination or other means could sort out fact from fantasy." The hypnotist testified that the child's later statements were not related to the hypnotic sessions, during which M had said nothing. The neighbor was found guilty as charged.

Children are vulnerable to suggestion. They can also appear to be telling the truth when reciting a precoached or parent-implanted story. They are not always certain of the source of their information, whether from school, a book, a parent, a friend, a dream, or a fantasy. Diamond's (1980) suggestion that "testimony by previously hypnotized witnesses should never be admitted into evidence" is well taken. All children have a tenuous grasp upon the truth, upon fact vs. fantasy, and upon their perceptions; therefore, hypnosis would render them incompetent to testify in any court matter. The California Supreme Court decision regarding the disqualification of previously hypnotized witnesses (*People v. Shirley,* 1982) may be a victory in this regard. Future cases of similar nature will determine the eventual course of this controversy.

## CHILD PSYCHIATRIC TESTIMONY WHICH BYPASSES THE CHILD'S APPEARANCE IN COURT

It is possible for the child psychiatrist to appear in lieu of the child providing: 1) the psychiatrist has interviewed the parent(s); 2) the psychiatrist qualifies by reason of training and experience as an "expert" witness (McCormick, 1972); 3) the psychiatrist states his or her expert opinion after being qualified; and 4) the psychiatrist is able to detail the statements and the observations from the child's interviews which formed the basis upon which he or she reached his or her expert opinion.

The technique of having the child psychiatrist-expert tell the story in court for the child, bypassing the child's direct testimony, may be a particularly useful one (Terr, 1980). This technique is particularly useful for infant-witnesses below the minimum age of competency, who in the psychiatrist's office or at home act out behaviorally or in play what had occurred to them (lending themselves to observation and subsequent expert interpretation to the court)(Terr, 1984). Infants and toddlers below age 3 deserve a voice in court, even though they themselves most likely would be disqualified if they were offered as witnesses. In cases of child abuse, sexual abuse, neglect, divorces in which one parent has not attached to the infant, and in psychic trauma, the infant victim may be interpreted to the court by the psychiatric expert.

Videotapes or live appearances of a young child in chambers—accompanied by the child psychiatrist, of course—can further aid in explaining an infant or toddler witness to the court.

A situation in which the testimony of the child psychiatric expert may be mandatory is a case in which a loyalty conflict or a fear on the part of the child would force the child to lie. Incest is a case in point (Nadelson & Rosenfeld, 1980). Children who have been involved in an incestuous relationship are repeatedly questioned, and often the charges must be dropped because the child becomes less and less willing to disrupt the entire fabric of the family by testifying (Defrancis, 1969). These children are often returned by the legal system to the very same conditions of family exploitation (Wald, 1975), worse off than before.

Wald (1975) has suggested that if neglect charges, rather than criminal charges, were filed in matters of abuse within the family, the child could be protected from the "trauma" of cross-examination. Another means of protection of the young incest victim would be the testimony of the child psychiatric expert witness in order to bypass the child's need to testify. In a criminal matter, however, if there are no other eyewitnesses and if there is no major confirming evidence (vaginal tears, the presence of semen, etc) the child, if of proper intelligence and so forth, will have to take the stand and be cross-examined. There are few ways to bypass a child's testimony, should it be demanded, in courts, which are absolutely strict about the rules of evidence (criminal courts, particularly).

Loyalty conflicts are strongest in children when they witness a crime perpetrated by someone upon whom they are dependent for nuture, even for life itself. The law provides that a spouse shall not be forced to testify against her or his marital partner. There are two reasons for this 1) to protect the intimacy that is essential to the marriage relationship; and 2) to protect the life and physical well being of the spouse, who may have to continue to live at close quarters with the other. Children are not protected by this kind of privilege, yet the two above reasons apply very meaningfully to them.

Let us consider, for instance, a child who was forced to testify against her father, who was accused of murdering her mother (Terr, 1980). The father was acquitted in court, and he became the sole provider and "protector" for this child-witness. In such situations the child would have best been served by a child-parent privilege rule. Unfortunately for the child, and perhaps also for the service of the truth, courts often determine that the right to cross-examine a child strongly outweighs the need for protection of the child-parent relationship. The court that forces a child to testify against his or her parent must painstakingly weigh the child's evidence given under these conditions. In such intense loyalty conflicts, the youngster's credibility must come into question.

The child psychiatric expert witness may be effectively used as a spokesperson for the child in custody of visitation disputes. Not only do these family law matters involve a child's sense of guilt about the family turmoil, loyalty conflicts, and "coaching" of the youngster by one or both parents (occasionally to the point of mental indoctrination, or "brainwashing"), but they also strongly depend upon the child's changing developmental needs. Children do not always "choose" the parent who meets their own best interests when they speak "in chambers" with the judge. An adolescent, for instance, may prefer living with the parent who does not discipline him or require him to do chores, yet this parent may not best serve his or her needs. Two children, ages 12 and 9, "chose" to be placed in the custody of their father, who had a very distant previous relationship with them, but who was now dying of cancer. They did not return to their mother, the far better parent of the two, for 3 years. They had made their choice out of guilt related to their father's terminal illness, and the court approved it. If bypassed as courtroom witnesses or as witnesses in the judge's chambers, children will not be placed in the extraordinarily difficult position of making choices in their own custody and visitation matters.

The child psychiatrist is fully able to stand-in for the child. An expert witness must be careful to state his or her psychiatric opinion after being qualified as an expert, and then may give those historical facts, quotes from the child, and observations of the child and the parents that led to his or her opinion. Formulations and recommendations are offered at the conclusion of direct testimony.

## THE CREDIBILITY OF CHILD WITNESSES

There are factors that diminish and factors that enhance the credibility of children who appear in court as witnesses. Trauma-related distortions of visual perception, time sense, and causality may diminish the weight given to the testimony of children. It is important to note, however, that studies of adult perception and memory, not related to trauma (Fischoff, 1975; Loftus, 1980), show that under ordinary circumstances, adults also misperceive and misremember. Loyalty conflicts may also weaken a child's testimony, especially in matters concerning his or her own family. On cross-examination young children often "flunk" tricky questions on numbers, dates, and details from their ordinary lives years before. Yet they may clearly remember a traumatic event, the event the court is considering.

Children lie relatively easily, especially when under pressure from those in authority. They also can be easily influenced by a parent into believing something that is not true. The expert witness may have to determine for him- or herself as best as possible whether a child is lying. Opinions about the child's truthfulness cannot be presented to a court unless the judge or jury asks for such an opinion. Even this may be subject to appeal because "the truth" is supposed to be the province only of the trier of fact ( judge or jury). In forming a psychiatric opinion before the trial, however, the psychiatric expert must take childhood lying into account. There is no sure way to detect subtle lying. Some of the following techniques may be helpful, however.

1) *Verification over time.* Have the child tell the story in several different interviews, taking careful notes of the child's language or recording the sessions on tape. If truthful, the wording must vary and the language must be child-language. The "facts," if the truth, will remain the same.
2) *Verification through dreams, reenactment, or post-traumatic play.* These items should coincide with the "facts" that the child victim relates.
3) *Verification through outside clues.* The child psychiatrist may prefer not to read police reports or other investigative data until after the child's interviews, so that he or she does not suggest the "facts" to the child and later incorporate them into the child's

testimony. However, once the child is interviewed, all ancillary data and investigative reports should be read and integrated by the psychiatrist.

4) *A history of reliability on the part of the child witness.* School records, camp records, family history, and the child's history should be checked for past incidents of lying or cheating.

There are two important factors that enhance a traumatized child's credibility as a witness: behavioral repetitions of the event and the absence of defensive "denial of external reality." The child victim can be expected to repeatedly play or reenact his or her horror in a way that is very close to the circumstances of the original event (Terr, 1981). (Exceptions may be made for victims of long-standing child abuse, deprivation, or incest, because the parental actions are repeated enough times that the child may eventually come to expect them, and thus is not overwhelmed in exactly the same way as in single-blow psychic trauma. Such victims are prone to massive personality change, psychic numbing, and occasionally, to multiple personalities. Reenactment and play remain important as symptoms in this chronically abused group.) Children who have been traumatized can give extraordinarily detailed accounts of the episode. Despite their frequent perceptual distortions, children often make better witnesses than adults who have suffered terrible experiences (Horowitz, 1976) due to the youngsters' keen eye for details and for full remembrance.

## THE CHILD'S DAY IN COURT

Despite the very obvious concerns on behalf of children regarding "retraumatization" in the courtroom, there can be some positive effects from being allowed to testify. Some of the older Chowchilla kidnapping victims were allowed to appear as criminal witnesses because they had suffered minor physical injuries or because they were old enough to testify without much risk of legal challenge (By common law in California until 1967, children aged 10 and over were assumed competent to testify). A few of the younger children who had not been allowed to testify complained that they had not been asked to appear before the Grand Jury or to appear in the kidnappers' trial. Courtroom appearance allows victims the opportunity to face a captor and to extract some vengeance. Although not demonstrated in Chowchilla because of the massiveness of the psychic trauma there, it may be true that giving a traumatized child victim the opportunity to help dispense justice may have some ameliorative effect.

In addition to directly helping a child express hostility toward someone who previously had robbed the child of all control, testifying may offer a child the chance to realistically reassess his or her tormentor. Jonathan and James Burgess, two boys held hostage by an escaped convict, Albert, had identified and sympathized with their captor after 11 hours of captivity. They were reluctant to appear in court to testify against Albert because they "liked him" and "felt sorry for him." When Jonathan did testify eventually, the experience proved invaluable to him. Jonathan told the court that Albert had sexually fondled him, and Albert looked straight back at Jonathan and repeatedly shook his head "no." Albert's attorney implied during cross-examination that Jonathan was lying. The boy, who knew that he was indeed speaking the truth, saw Albert for the first time as a hardened unrepentant criminal. Jonathan later stated to the child psychiatrist that he had been "cured" of his liking for Albert. More importantly, his unconscious identification with the aggressor was destroyed that day in the courtroom.

A current trend today in considering children's testimony is to allow child witnesses to sexual abuse to appear on closed circuit TV. This option would be a helpful possibility for some, but not all, youngsters who appear as witnesses—not only in sex cases. Certainly some children are too embarrassed or too afraid to candidly face their tormentor in public. But on the other hand, the child may not thereby achieve the direct "revenge" offered by looking directly at the accused and telling the story. Using TV as one option could be the best way of approaching this procedure, if US Sixth Amendment Rights are not found to be violated in the process.

## DISCUSSION

Child witnesses are being called into our courts in increasing numbers, yet no one has looked scientifically at the effect of courtroom witnessing on youngsters. Does it help? Does it hurt? What protections are needed?

First, we will need good research studies to learn what we are facing. Next, we need better procedures. Finally, we must consider prevention of situations that require children to come into court in a harmful way.

Every child witness should be allowed the use of a court appointed legal counsellor whose business it is to protect that youngster. This would put a number of lawyers to work, but the risks far outweigh the expenses. Children require protection from the moment the police or law enforcement interrogation begins. They must be sheltered from suggestive questioning, hypnosis, Amytal interviewing, or promises of happy consequences for giving evidence against their families. Such protection might come about if police quizzing of children was monitored on a sporadic, random basis by mental health professionals.

Few children ever come to court. However, those children who do rarely are debriefed. Ideally children would be prepared by a child psychiatrist before appearing in court. They would be "debriefed" afterward. The preparation aspect has been stressed by various experts (Berliner & Barbieri, 1984; Goodman, 1984). But discussion afterward is just as important (Pynoos & Eth, 1984). By discussing with a psychiatrist what happened in court, the young witness may be able to put what occurred into some context, rather than into a fantasy based more on inner, than on outer, realities.

At times, child witnesses may be entirely bypassed by using the child psychiatrist, instead. For children too young, too developmentally immature, or too disabled, or for those too torn with loyalty conflicts to testify properly or coherently, the child psychiatrist would be a substitute, telling the child's story for the child.

A child-parent privilege would be very helpful (Terr, 1986), and it would seem important, to us at least, that legislatures consider passing such a privilege into law. In instances where children wish not to testify against a parent, they should not be forced to do so. This would avoid many cases in which youngsters are impelled to lie on the witness stand. It would also mitigate against youngsters suddenly changing their stories before the trial is to take place. Youngsters are aware of the private stories inside their families. They are also vulnerable to retaliatory physical violence. Thus, the reasoning that allows the wife-husband testimonial privilege, a privilege that is acknowledged under US law, applies even more strongly to children.

We as a society must do better with prevention and thereby lessen the number of children who have to appear as witness. Careful daycare licensing, better parent education, more thorough monitoring, and national collection and sharing of information regarding those with records for having mishandled children would help. Collection of license numbers and social security numbers by pediatricians of the parents of all children entering their practices would drastically cut down "successful" parent child-snatching cases. Other preventive ideas will come along and must be considered. Sadly, however, there will always be the need for some "child witnesses."

## REFERENCES

*American Jurisprudence* (2nd ed.). (1976). 81, Witnesses S88-98. San Francisco: Bancroft-Whitney.

Berliner, L., & Barbieri, M. (1984). The testimony of the child victim of assault. *Journal of Social Issues, 40,* 125–137.

Black, H. (1968). *Black's Law Dictionary,* St. Paul: West.

DeFrancis, V. (1969). *Protecting the child victims of sex crimes committed by adults.* Denver: The American Humane Association.

Diamond, B. (1980). Inherent problems in the use of pretrial hypnosis on a prospective witness. *California Law Review, 68,* 313–349.

Fischoff, B. (1975). Hindsight-Foresight: The effect of outcome knowledge on judgment under uncertainty. *Journal of Experimental Psychology: Human Perception and Performance, 1,* 288–299.

Goodman, G. (1984). The child witness: Conclusions and future directions for research and legal practice. *Journal of Social Issues, 40,* 157–175.

Hollaris v. Jankowski, 315 Ill App 154, 42 NE 2nd 859 (1942).

Horowitz, M. (1976). *Stress response syndromes*. New York: Jason Aronson.

Knab v. Alden's Irving Park, Inc. 49 Ill App 2d 371, 199 NE 2d 815 (1964).

Loftus, E. (1980). *Memory*. Reading, MA: Addison Wesley.

*Los Angeles Daily Journal.* (1987, June 3). p. 1.

McCormick (1972). *McCormick's handbook of the law of evidence* (2nd ed.).

Nadelson, C., & Rosenfeld, A. (1980). Sexual misuse of children. In D. Shetky & E. Benedek (Eds.), *Child psychiatry and the law* (pp. 89-106). New York: Brunner/Mazel.

People v. Shirley, 31 Cal. 3d 18, 53, 1982.

Pynoos, R., & Eth, S. (1984). The child as witness to homicide. *Journal of Social Issues, 40,* 87-108.

Rosche v. McCoy, 397, Pa 615, 156 A 2d 307, 81 ALR 2d 377, 1959.

State v. Belton, 24 SC 185 (1885).

Taub-Katz, J., & Katz, A. (1980, October). The child on the witness stand: Psychiatric and legal considerations. Paper presented at the annual meeting American Academy of Child Psychiatry.

Terr, L. (1980). The child as a witness. In D. Shetky & E. Benedek (Eds.), *Child psychiatry and the law* (pp. 207-221). New York: Brunner/Mazel.

Terr, L. (1981a). Psychic trauma in children: Observations following the Chowchilla schoolbus kidnapping. *American Journal of Psychiatry, 138,* 14-19.

Terr, L. (1981b). "Forbidden games": Post-traumatic child's play. *Journal of the American Academy of Child Psychiatry, 20,* 741-760.

Terr, L. (1983a). Chowchilla revisited: The effects of psychic trauma four years after the kidnapping of a schoolbus. *American Journal of Psychiatry, 140,* 1543-1550.

Terr, L. (1983b). Time sense following psychic trauma: A clinical study of ten adults and twenty children. *American Journal of Orthopsychiatry, 53,* 244-261.

Terr, L. (1984). The baby in court. In J. Call, E. Galenson, & R. Tyson (Eds.), *Frontiers of infant psychiatry II* (pp. 490-494). New York: Basic Books.

Terr, L. (1986). The child psychiatrist and the child witness: Traveling companions by necessity, if not by design. *Journal of the American Academy of Child Psychiatry, 25,* 462-472.

Wald, M. (1975). State intervention on behalf of "neglected" children: A search for realistic standards. *Stanford Law Review, 27,* 985-1040.

Wheeler v. United States, 159 U.S. 523, 40 L Ed 244, 16 SCt 93 (1897).

Whitehead v. Stith, 268 Ky 703, 105 SW 2d 834 (1937).

# EPILOGUE

The setting is a small town in mid-America two days before high school graduation, June 1959. Two graduating seniors, one an all-conference halfback and the other a math whiz, pull a prank. Late at night they sneak three phonograph records with "dirty" lyrics into the local radio station, wait for the disc jockey to step into the men's room, and put their records into the pile.

On their way out a window, the boys are caught. But before the night watchman can warn the station engineer, one of the sexually suggestive ditties is on the air. The young men are turned over to the police, who arrest the 18-year-old football player and take him off to jail. The math whiz, 17-years-old, 5 months younger than his friend, is let go.

The halfback is charged with "trespassing" and "malicious mischief." The police phone the principal of the high school, who denies the senior his graduation ceremonies as well as his diploma. The principal also calls the director of admissions of the college that already accepted the young man as an entering freshman. The principal tells the college to change its mind.

This case exemplifies what has been presented in this book. Does the age 18 really separate two young men, designating one as an arrested criminal and nongraduate as opposed to his friend, the "juvenile"? Why must the football player pay the price thrice over while the 17-year-old goes scot-free? And what punishment hurts the halfback worse: the legally sanctioned overnight jailing and criminal charges, or the informally arranged refusal to certify the boy's graduation and the even more informally arranged attempt to block his college matriculation? Not all age-dictated responses to children reside in our courts and lawmaking chambers. They also occupy most of the folkways and institutions that deal with children.

It is our position that the ages at which children's "crimes" are defined and their rights proclaimed are by and large arbitrary. Statutes often ignore the changing developmental capacities of the growing person and cannot be tailored easily to individual delinquents. Furthermore, statutes reflect their times and often arise from custom or current need, rather than from any concern for the development of children and youth. If events, in and of themselves, can "condemn" youngsters and if their birthdays, alone, can "hang" them, few adults in positions of authority may ever grasp what emotional stages and cognitive levels underlie and determine young people's actions within their families and in society.

We agree that age can be a simple way to determine children's rights and responsibilities. We acknowledge that in a very rough fashion, society has identified certain suitable markers in the ages of 7, 14, and 21 $\pm$ 1. But we have argued in this report that developmental level is a far more sensible and humane way of judging rights and responsibilities than is chronological age. When to use one and when to use the other depends on circumstances. Serious situations, especially those involving the courts, require a developmental approach. Laws mandate age rather than stage. But the applications and enforcement of these laws may necessitate considering the child's stage on a case-by-case basis.

In this report we have brought together materials from cultural and judicial practice that were, up to now, unavailable in a single source. We have also brought together some materials and facts only recently available to the field of child psychiatry. We believe that by presenting composites of these data and ideas, we can provide a rational and a reference scheme for the better handling of questions regarding young persons' rights and responsibilities.

We wish to encourage child psychiatrists to enter the domain in which social and legal plans for children are conceived and carried out. Child psychiatry, more than any other field, has at hand the outlook and tools to conduct stage and phase evaluations of children's capacities. The child psychiatric approach must be conveyed to our juries, judges and lawmakers so that more sensible rules and rulings are made. Whenever there is a question of a child's rights and responsibilities, the young person should be allowed the option of a developmental evaluation.

Child psychiatry combines the practical approach of medicine with the developmentalist's mandate to think in "stages." Ours is the profession most expert in assessing physical, emotional, cognitive, and social aspects of both normal and disordered development. Other fields that train and offer experience in child development, of course, will also contribute much to any decisions reached regarding children's rights and responsibilities. But we in child psychiatry turn first to our own professional colleagues, asking them to begin taking part in any judicial or legislative processes having to do with what is allowed or expected of children.

We believe we have offered a start, but only a start. It will be up to others to research and fill out the specific issues in the field of children's rights. Our main message, however—to take the developmental perspective—is, we believe, well-demonstrated.

To conclude we offer a brief follow-up to the case report that began our epilogue. The young football player did not graduate with his class, though he did receive a diploma in the mail 1 year after he began appealing to the school board. The college did take him in as a freshman despite what the high school principal had said. The town prosecutor eventually dropped his criminal charges against the lad because, he told him, his record was "clean" and the "community had stayed quiet." America took up the "sexual revolution" and began broadcasting to its teenagers tunes with lyrics like "Get down. Get down. Ugh" or "Do it to me baby" or "Do it in the middle of the road," all much more suggestive than the ditties which had been broadcast in this case report. The young man excelled in college and his subsequent professional education, eventually becoming successful in a professional field.

# GAP COMMITTEES AND MEMBERSHIP

COMMITTEE ON ADOLESCENCE
Clarice J. Kestenbaum, New York, NY,
   Chairperson
Hector R. Bird, New York, NY
Ian A. Canino, New York, NY
Warren J. Gadpaille, Denver, CO
Michael G. Kalogerakis, New York, NY
Paulina F. Kernberg, White Plains, NY
Richard C. Marohn, Chicago, IL
Silvio J. Onesti, Jr., Belmont, MA


COMMITTEE ON AGING
Gene D. Cohen, Washington, DC
   Chairperson
Eric D. Caine, Rochester, NY
Charles M. Gaitz, Houston, TX
Gabe J. Maletta, Minneapolis, MN
Robert J. Nathan, Philadelphia, PA
George H. Pollock, Chicago, IL
Kenneth M. Sakauye, New Orleans, LA
Charles A. Shamoian, Larchmont, NY
F. Conyers Thompson, Jr., Atlanta, GA


COMMITTEE ON ALCOHOLISM AND THE
   ADDICTIONS
Edward J. Khantzian, Haverhill, MA,
   Chairperson
Margaret H. Bean-Bayog, Lexington,
   MA
Richard J. Frances, Newark, NJ
Sheldon I. Miller, Newark, NJ
Robert B. Millman, New York, NY
Steven M. Mirin, Westwood, MA

Edgar P. Nace, Dallas, TX
Norman L. Paul, Lexington, MA
Peter Steinglass, Washington, DC
John S. Tamerin, Greenwich, CT


COMMITTEE ON COLLEGE STUDENTS
Myron B. Liptzin, Chapel Hill, NC,
   Chairperson
Robert L. Arnstein, Hamden, CT
Varda Backus, La Jolla, CA
Harrison P. Eddy, New York, NY
Malkah Tolpin Notman, Brookline,
   MA
Gloria C. Onque, Pittsburgh, PA
Elizabeth Aub Reid, Cambridge, MA
Earle Silber, Chevy Chase, MD
Tom G. Stauffer, White Plains, NY


COMMITTEE ON CULTURAL PSYCHIATRY
Ezra E.H. Griffith, New Haven, CT,
   Chairperson
Edward F. Foulks, New Orleans, LA
Pedro Ruiz, Houston, TX
Ronald M. Wintrob, Providence, RI
Joe Yamamoto, Los Angeles, CA


COMMITTEE ON THE FAMILY
Herta A. Guttman, Montreal, Que.,
   Chairperson
W. Robert Beavers, Dallas, TX
Ellen M. Berman, Merrion, PA
Lee Combrinck-Graham, Evanston,
   IL

119

Ira D. Glick, New York, NY
Frederick Gottlieb, Los Angeles, CA
Henry U. Grunebaum, Cambridge,
  MA
Ann L. Price, Hartford, CT
Lyman C. Wynne, Rochester, NY


COMMITTEE ON GOVERNMENTAL
  AGENCIES
William W. Van Stone, Palo
  Alto, CA, Chairperson
James P. Cattell, San Diego, CA
Thomas L. Clannon, San Francisco,
  CA
Sidney S. Goldensohn, New York, NY
Naomi Heller, Washington, DC
Roger Peele, Washington, DC
John P. D. Shemo, Charlottesville, VA


COMMITTEE ON HANDICAPS
William H. Sack, Portland, OR,
  Chairperson
Norman R. Bernstein, Cambridge,
  MA
Meyer S. Gunther, Wilmette, IL
Betty J. Pfefferbaum, Houston, TX
William A. Sonis, Philadelphia, PA
Margaret L. Stuber, Los Angeles, CA
George Tarjan, Los Angeles, CA
Thomas G. Webster, Washington, DC
Henry H. Work, Bethesda, MD


COMMITTEE ON HUMAN SEXUALITY
Bertram H. Schaffner, New York, NY,
  Chairperson
Paul L. Adams, Galveston, TX
Johanna A. Hoffman, Scottsdale, AZ
Joan A. Lang, Galveston, TX
Stuart E. Nichols, New York, NY
Harris B. Peck, New Rochelle, NY
John P. Spiegel, Waltham, MA
Terry S. Stein, East Lansing, MI

COMMITTEE ON INTERNATIONAL
  RELATIONS
Vamik D. Volkan, Charlottesville, VA,
  Chairperson
Francis F. Barnes, Washington, DC
Robert M. Dorn, El Macero, CA
John S. Kafka, Washington, DC
Otto F. Kernberg, White Plains, NY
John E. Mack, Chestnut Hill, MA
Rita R. Rogers, Palos Verdes Estates, CA
Stephen B. Shanfield, San Antonio, TX


COMMITTEE ON MEDICAL EDUCATION
Stephen C. Scheiber, Deerfield, IL,
  Chairperson
Gene Abroms, Ardmore, PA
Charles M. Culver, Hanover, NH
Steven L. Dubovsky, Denver, CO
Saul I. Harrison, Torrance, CA
David R. Hawkins, Chicago, IL
Harold I. Lief, Philadelphia, PA
Carol Nadelson, Boston, MA
Carolyn B. Robinowitz, Washington,
  DC
Sidney L. Werkman, Washington, DC
Veva H. Zimmerman, New York, NY


COMMITTEE ON MENTAL HEALTH
  SERVICES
Jose Maria Santiago, Tucson, AZ,
  Chairperson
John M. Hamilton, Columbia, MD
W. Walter Menninger, Topeka, KS
Steven S. Sharfstein, Baltimore, MD
Herzl R. Spiro, Milwaukee, WI
William L. Webb, Jr., Hartford, CT
George F. Wilson, Somerville, NJ
Jack A. Wolford, Pittsburgh, PA


COMMITTEE ON PLANNING AND
  MARKETING
Robert W. Gibson, Towson, MD,
  Chairperson
Allan Beigel, Tucson, AZ

Robert J. Campbell, New York, NY
Doyle I. Carson, Dallas, TX
Paul J. Fink, Philadelphia, PA
Robert S. Garber, Longboat Key, FL
Harvey L. Ruben, New Haven, CT
Melvin Sabshin, Washington, DC
Michael R. Zales, Quechee, VT

COMMITTEE ON PREVENTIVE PSYCHIATRY
Stephen Fleck, New Haven, CT,
  Chairperson
Viola W. Bernard, New York, NY
Naomi Rae-Grant, London, Ont.
Morton M. Silverman, Chicago, IL
Warren T. Vaughan, Jr., Portola Valley,
  CA
Anne Marie Wolf-Schatz,
  Conshohocken, PA

COMMITTEE ON PSYCHIATRY AND THE
  COMMUNITY
Kenneth Minkoff, Woburn, MA,
  Chairperson
C. Knight Aldrich, Charlottesville, VA
David G. Greenfeld, Guilford, CT
H. Richard Lamb, Los Angeles, CA
John C. Nemiah, Hanover, NH
Rebecca L. Potter, Tucson, AZ
Alexander S. Rogawski, Los Angeles,
  CA
John J. Schwab, Louisville, KY
John A. Talbott, Baltimore, MD
Charles B. Wilkinson, Kansas City, MO

COMMITTEE ON PSYCHIATRY AND LAW
Jonas R. Rappeport, Baltimore, MD,
  Chairperson
Park E. Dietz, Charlottesville, VA
John Donnelly, Hartford, CT
Carl P. Malmquist, Minneapolis, MN
Herbert C. Modlin, Topeka, KS
Phillip J. Resnick, Cleveland, OH
Loren H. Roth, Pittsburgh, PA

Joseph Satten, San Francisco, CA
William D. Weitzel, Lexington, KY
Howard V. Zonana, New Haven, CT

COMMITTEE ON PSYCHIATRY AND
  RELIGION
Albert J. Lubin, Woodside, CA,
  Chairperson
Sidney Furst, Bronx, NY
Richard C. Lewis, New Haven, CT
Earl A. Loomis, Jr., Augusta, GA
Abigail R. Ostow, Belmont, MA
Mortimer Ostow, Bronx, NY
Sally K. Severino, White Plains, NY
Clyde R. Snyder, Fayetteville, NC

COMMITTEE ON PSYCHIATRY IN INDUSTRY
Barrie S. Greiff, Newton, MA,
  Chairperson
Peter L. Brill, Radnor, PA
Duane Q. Hagen, St. Louis, MO
R. Edward Huffman, Asheville, NC
David E. Morrison, Palatine, IL
David B. Robbins, Chappaqua, NY
Jay B. Rohrlich, New York, NY
Clarence J. Rowe, St. Paul, MN
Jeffrey L. Speller, Cambridge, MA

COMMITTEE ON PSYCHOPATHOLOGY
David A. Adler, Boston, MA,
  Chairperson
Jeffrey Berlant, Summit, NJ
Robert A. Dorwart, Cambridge, MA
Robert E. Drake, Hanover, NH
James M. Ellison, Watertown, MA
Howard H. Goldman, Potomac, MD

COMMITTEE ON PUBLIC EDUCATION
Keith H. Johansen, Dallas, TX,
  Chairperson
Jack W. Bonner, III, Asheville, NY
Steven E. Katz, New York, NY

Othilda M. Krug, Cincinnati, OH
Judith Landau-Stanton, Rochester, NY
Alan I. Levenson, Tucson, AZ
Ruth W. Lidz, Woodbridge, CT
Orlando B. Lightfoot, Boston, MA
Norman L. Loux, Sellersville, PA
John A. MacLeod, Cincinnati, OH
Leo Madow, Philadelphia, PA
Charles A. Malone, Barrington, RI
Peter A. Martin, Lake Orion, MI
Ake Mattsson, Charlottesville, VA
Alan A. McLean, Westport, CT
David Mendell, Houston, TX
Roy W. Menninger, Topeka, KS
Mary E. Mercer, Nyack, NY
Derek Miller, Chicago, IL
Richard D. Morrill, Boston, MA
Joseph D. Noshpitz, Washington, DC
Bernard L. Pacella, New York, NY
Herbert Pardes, New York, NY
Marvin E. Perkins, Salem, VA
David N. Ratnavale, Bethesda, MD
Richard E. Renneker, West Los
    Angeles, CA
W. Donald Ross, Cincinnati, OH
Lester H. Rudy, Chicago, IL
Donald J. Scherl, Brooklyn, NY
Charles Shagrass, Philadelphia, PA
Miles F. Shore, Boston, MA
Albert J. Silverman, Ann Arbor, MI
Benson R. Snyder, Cambridge, MA
David A. Soskis, Bala Cynwyd, PA
Jeanne Spurlock, Washington, DC
Brandt F. Steele, Denver, CO
Alan A. Stone, Cambridge, MA
Perry C. Talkington, Dallas, TX
Bryce Templeton, Philadelphia, PA
Prescott W. Thompson, Beaverton, OR
Joe P. Tupin, Sacramento, CA
John A. Turner, San Francisco, CA
Gene L. Usdin, New Orleans, LA
Andrew S. Watson, Ann Arbor, MI
Joseph B. Wheelwright, Kentfield, CA
Robert L. Williams, Houston, TX
Paul Tyler Wilson, Bethesda, MD

Sherwyn M. Woods, Los Angeles, CA
Kent A. Zimmerman, Menlo Park, CA
Israel Zwerling, Philadelphia, PA

LIFE MEMBERS
C. Knight Aldrich, Charlottesville, VA
Bernard Bandler, Cambridge, MA
Walter E. Barton, Hartland, VT
Viola W. Bernard, New York, NY
Murray Bowen, Chevy Chase, MD
Henry W. Brosin, Tucson, AZ
John Donnelly, Hartford, CT
Merrill T. Eaton, Omaha, NE
O. Spurgeon English, Narberth, PA
Stephen Fleck, New Haven, CT
Jerome Frank, Baltimore, MD
Robert S. Garber, Longboat Key, FL
Robert I. Gibson, Towson, MD
Paul E. Huston, Iowa City, IA
Margaret M. Lawrence, Pomona, NY
Harold I. Lief, Philadelphia, PA
Morris A. Lipton, Chapel Hill, NC
Judd Marmor, Los Angeles, CA
Karl A. Menninger, Topeka, KS
Herbert C. Modlin, Topeka, KS
John C. Nemiah, Hanover, NH
Alexander S. Rogawski, Los Angeles, CA
Mabel Ross, Sun City, AZ
Julius Schreiber, Washington, DC
Robert E. Switzer, Dunn Loring, VA
George Tarjan, Los Angeles, CA
Jack A. Wolford, Pittsburgh, PA
Henry H. Work, Bethesda, MD


BOARD OF DIRECTORS

OFFICERS

*President*
Jerry M. Lewis
Timberlawn Foundation
P.O. Box 270789
Dallas, TX 75227